W9-BLZ-480

Geometric Transformations

VOLUME 1

Euclidean and Affine Transformations

ACADEMIC PAPERBACKS*

EDITED BY Henry Booker, D. Allan Bromley, Nicholas DeClaris, W. Magnus, Alvin Nason, and A. Shenitzer

BIOLOGY

Design and Function at the Threshold of Life: The Viruses
  HEINZ FRAENKEL-CONRAT
The Evolution of Genetics   ARNOLD W. RAVIN
Isotopes in Biology   GEORGE WOLF
Life: Its Nature, Origin, and Development   A. I. OPARIN
Time, Cells, and Aging   BERNARD L. STREHLER

ENGINEERING

A Vector Approach to Oscillations   HENRY BOOKER
Dynamic Programming and Modern Control Theory   RICHARD
  BELLMAN and ROBERT KALABA

MATHEMATICS

Finite Permutation Groups   HELMUT WIELANDT
Elements of Abstract Harmonic Analysis   GEORGE BACHMAN
The Method of Averaging Functional Corrections: Theory and
  Applications   A. Yu. LUCHKA
Geometric Transformations (in two volumes)   P. S. MODENOV
  and A. S. PARKHOMENKO
Representation Theory of Finite Groups   MARTIN BURROW
Introduction to p-Adic Numbers and Valuation Theory
  GEORGE BACHMAN
Linear Operators in Hilbert Space   WERNER SCHMEIDLER
Noneuclidean Geometry   HERBERT MESCHKOWSKI
Quadratic Forms and Matrices   N. V. YEFIMOV

PHYSICS

Crystals: Their Role in Nature and in Science   CHARLES BUNN
Elementary Dynamics of Particles   H. W. HARKNESS
Elementary Plane Rigid Dynamics   H. W. HARKNESS
Mössbauer Effect: Principles and Applications
  GUNTHER K. WERTHEIM
Potential Barriers in Semiconductors   B. R. GOSSICK
Principles of Vector Analysis   JERRY B. MARION

*Most of these volumes are also available in a cloth bound edition.

Geometric Transformations

P. S. MODENOV and A. S. PARKHOMENKO

VOLUME 1

Euclidean and Affine Transformations

Translated and adapted from the first Russian edition by

MICHAEL B. P. SLATER

Published in cooperation with the
SURVEY OF
RECENT EAST EUROPEAN MATHEMATICAL LITERATURE
A project conducted by
ALFRED L. PUTNAM AND IZAAK WIRSZUP
Department of Mathematics,
The University of Chicago, under a
grant from the National Science Foundation

ACADEMIC PRESS   New York and London

First published in the Russian language under the title
Geometricheskie Preobrazovaniya
in 1961 by Izdatel'stvo Moskovskogo Universitet,
Moscow, U.S.S.R.

ACADEMIC PRESS INC.
111 Fifth Avenue, New York, New York 10003

United Kingdom Edition published by
ACADEMIC PRESS INC. (LONDON) LTD.
Berkeley Square House, London W.1

LIBRARY OF CONGRESS CATALOG CARD NUMBER: 65-25004

PRINTED IN THE UNITED STATES OF AMERICA

Preface to Volume 1
of the English Edition

This is the first volume of a two-volume translation of the Russian book *Geometric Transformations,* by Modenov and Parkhomenko. This volume embraces Chapters I –IV; Volume 2 *(Projective Transformations)* contains the translation of the original Chapters V and VI.

The treatment is elementary, and should be accessible to the high school senior. The prerequisites amount to some familiarity with Euclidean geometry, including the use of coordinates, elementary trigonometry, and linear equations (up to determinants). A little knowledge of vectors and conics might also be helpful. However, the material covered or referred to ranges much further, and should be of interest to a very broad spectrum of readers, from high school senior to college teacher.

This book is not designed to be a standard text. As will be seen from the introduction, the material covered is not usually included in the curriculum, and its style is more suitable for browsing than for systematic class study. The purpose of the book is rather to introduce the reader to a fascinating and not at all difficult area of geometry, at the same time acquainting him painlessly with some of the simpler methods and concepts of advanced mathematics. Since the topic is one for which everyone will have some intuitive feeling, and the exposition is consistently straightforward, there is no danger that the reader will find himself suddenly out of his depth.

The Russian authors suggest that this book can best serve as extracurricular material for geometry seminars in universities and teacher-training colleges, as extra background material for school mathematics clubs (under a teacher's guidance). This translation might well serve similar purposes in American schools and colleges.

Chicago, Illinois   M. SLATER
1965

Translator's Note

The translation is quite free. Although it retains all of the original text, it recasts many passages and in several sections includes additional background discussion and motivation. Apart from the Appendix to Chapter II, however, the section headings are the same, and in the same order, as in the original. Wherever I have added to or changed the original, I have tried to remain consistently within its spirit. The burden of responsibility for all deviations from the original must rest entirely on me.

M. S.

Preface to the Russian Edition

This book is intended for use in geometry seminars in universities and teacher-training colleges. It may also be used as supplementary reading by high school teachers who wish to extend their range of knowledge. Finally, many sections may be used as source material for school mathematics clubs under the guidance of a teacher.

The subject matter is those transformations of the plane that preserve the fundamental figures of geometry: straight lines and circles. In particular, we discuss orthogonal, affine, projective, and similarity transformations, and inversions.

The treatment is elementary, though in a number of instances (where a synthetic treatment seems more cumbersome) coordinate methods are used. A little use is also made of vector algebra, but the text here is self-contained.

In order to clarify a number of points, we give some elementary facts from projective geometry; also, in the addendum to Chapter I of Volume 2 (the topology of the projective plane), the structure of the projective plane is examined in greater detail.

The authors feel obliged to express their thanks to Professor V. G. Boltyanskii, who carefully read the manuscript and made a number of valuable suggestions. They also wish to thank Miss V. S. Kapustina for editing the manuscript and removing many inadequacies of presentation. They would like also to say that Chapter II of Volume 2 was written with the help of an article on inversion written by V. V. Kucherenko, a second-year physics student. It is to him that we owe the elegant proof of the fundamental theorem that any circle transformation can be represented as the product of an inversion and a similarity transformation, and also as the product of an inversion and a rotation (or a reflection).

Moscow   THE AUTHORS
January 1961

Contents

Chapter III.   Similarity Transformations

Chapter IV.   Affine Transformations

Introduction

In the study of a number of questions in geometry, such as the proofs of certain theorems, the solution of problems of construction, and the examination of geometric figures, high school courses in geometry use certain types of transformation: reflections, rotations, translations, similarities, and inversions.

We shall give a general definition of the concept of a transformation and shall then examine those transformations that are most important for elementary geometry: orthogonal, affine, and projective transformations, and inversions.

The examination of these types of transformation is important for two reasons:

1. These transformations are the "simplest," in the sense that they preserve the fundamental material of geometry: line segments and angles are preserved by orthogonal transformations; straight lines by orthogonal, affine, and projective transformations; and lines and circles taken together by inversions.

2. The division of geometry into elementary, affine, projective, and other "geometries" is determined by those geometric properties of the figures which are required to remain fixed. Thus each "geometry" is associated with a group of transformations: precisely those that leave the required properties invariant. For example, elementary geometry is concerned

with such properties of geometric figures as angles between lines, lengths, parallelism, and, in fact, all those properties of figures which are preserved under translation (and similarity). Affine geometry studies precisely those properties of geometric figures that are preserved under affine transformations: the straightness of lines, parallelism, the ratio between the lengths of two segments on a line, and so on; however, affine transformations do not, in general, preserve lengths or angles, and affine geometry does not therefore concern itself with such metrical properties of figures. Projective geometry studies those properties that are preserved by projective transformations. Such properties are, for example, the straightness of a line, the cross ratio of four points on a line (in particular, harmonicity), and others. But projective transformations may change lengths and angles, and even take parallel lines into nonparallel ones. Thus in projective geometry there is no concept of parallelism, just as in affine geometry (and also projective geometry) there is no concept of length or angle.

We note finally that it is sometimes possible to replace the study of some more general transformation by the study of an affine transformation which is a sufficiently good approximation to it. This is done in hydromechanics when investigating a complicated flow of liquid, in the theory of elasticity when studying the deformation of solid bodies, and in other fields.

On the whole, we shall confine our attention to transformations of the plane. The investigation of transformations of 3-space is analogous, and we shall only consider it separately when it presents special features of its own.

CHAPTER I

General Definitions

I. Sets and Functions

There are two concepts in mathematics in terms of which the basic definitions and theorems may be formulated in the most exact way possible. These are the concepts of a set and a function. These concepts themselves are regarded in mathematics as fundamental; that is, they are not defined in terms of anything else. Their meaning is commonly made clear by examples, and this is how we too shall start.

As one example of a set, consider a circle. This is the set of all those points of the plane that lie at a certain given distance from a given point (the center). As another example, consider the set of all points M lying within a triangle ABC. This is a set characterized by the following property: for each point M in it, M and A lie on the same side of the line BC, M and B lie on the same side of the line CA, and M and C lie on the same side of the line AB.

Lines and planes can be defined in mathematics as sets of points in space satisfying quite definite conditions. In what follows we shall identify lines and planes with the sets of points of which they consist, although in elementary geometry all these concepts (point, line, plane) are regarded as fundamental.

We meet with the concept of a function very early in our study of mathematics: the polynomial

$$y = a_0 x^n + a_1 x^{n-1} + \cdots + a_n$$

gives us a very simple example of an algebraic function. Examples of more complicated functions are

$$y = a^x, \qquad y = \log_a x, \qquad y = \sin x$$

$$y = \tan x.$$

In examining a function we must always pay attention to two questions:

1. What is the set of values for which the function is defined (the *domain of definition* of the function)?
2. What is the set of values assumed by the function?

For example, if we restrict our attention to real numbers, the domain of definition of the function $y = x^2$ is the set of all real numbers, while its range of values is the set of all nonnegative numbers.

For the function $y = \log x$ the domain of definition is the set of all positive numbers, and the range of values is the set of all real numbers.

For the function $y = \sin x$ the domain is the set of all real numbers, while the range of values is the set of all those y whose absolute value does not exceed 1. For the function $y = \log \sin x$ the domain is the set of all those numbers which lie in an interval of the form

$$2k\pi < x < (2k + 1)\pi$$

where k is any integer. The range is the set of all nonpositive numbers.

If we go one step further to the function $y = \sqrt{\log \sin x}$ we find that the domain is the set of points of the form

$$\chi = (\pi/2) + 2k\pi$$

where k is any integer, and the range of values is the set whose only member is zero.

We shall not here consider the general properties of sets and functions. For such an account see Walter Rudin, "Principles of Mathematical Analysis," McGraw-Hill, New York, 1953.[1]

The examples we gave above can also be regarded from the following point of view: the function $y = x^2$ maps the set of all the points on one line (the x axis) onto the set of all the points of a half line (the nonnegative part of the x axis): the map is that map which carries a point $M(x)$ into the point $M'(x^2)$, where the notation $M(x)$ refers to the point M whose coordinate on the x axis is x. For example, the point $M(3)$ is carried into the point $M'(9)$, while the point $M'(9)$ is carried into the point $M''(81)$, and so on.

The function $y = \log x$ maps the half line $(x > 0)$ onto the whole line, and similarly for the other functions.

A generalization of the ordinary concept of function in geometry is given by the concepts of mappings and transformations. Here the domain of definition and the range of values are no longer taken to be sets of numbers but sets of points on a line or a plane or in space.

For example, under a similitude with center O and coefficient $k > 0$, each point M of the plane is mapped into the point M' of the ray OM for which

$$OM'/OM = k,$$

while O is carried into itself. Here both the domain and range of the transformation are the entire plane (Fig. 1).

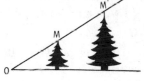

Fig. 1

[1] The Russian text recommends a book not available in English: P. S. Aleksandrov, "Vvedenie v obshchuyu teoriyu mnozhestv i funktsii," Gostekhizdat, 1947. A German translation is: P. S. Alexandroff, "Einführung in die Mengenlehre der Reelen Funktionen," Deutscher Verlag der Wissenschaften, 1956.

2. Mappings

We start our discussion of the theory of geometric transformations with some general definitions. These will appear
rather abstract because they refer to sets the nature of whose
elements will not, for the time being, concern us. We do this so
that our definitions include mappings of lines, planes, and the
whole of space, as well as mappings of subsets of such sets.
In addition, we shall later need the concept of a transformation
applied to a geometric object beyond the scope of elementary
geometry.

When the reader first looks at the definitions given below,
he will find it useful to imagine the sets which are mentioned as,
for example, the set of all points on a line or a plane and to
think of the mappings as being some simple and well-defined
transformations (for instance, a reflection of the plane in the
y axis, or a rotation of the plane about the origin, if the set he
is thinking of is the plane). The reader should first read the
definitions, then work carefully through all the examples illus-
trating them, and then read through the definitions a second
time.

Definition.   A mapping α of a set $\mathfrak{W}$ into a set $\mathfrak{W}'$ is a
correspondence under which every member M of $\mathfrak{W}$ is associated with a perfectly well-defined member M' of $\mathfrak{W}'$.

The element M' is called the *image* of M, while M is called an
inverse image of M' under the mapping α. If M' is the image of
M under the mapping α, we shall write

$$M' = \alpha(M).$$

Let A be any subset of the set $\mathfrak{W}$ and A' the totality of all
those elements of $\mathfrak{W}'$ which are images of elements of the set A;
then we call A', which is a subset of $\mathfrak{W}'$, the *image* of the set A
(under the mapping α).

If B' is a subset of $\mathfrak{W}'$, then the set B of all those elements of

$\mathfrak{W}$ whose images are members of B' is called the *complete inverse image* of the set B' under the mapping α.

If *every* element of $\mathfrak{W}'$ has at least one element of $\mathfrak{W}$ corresponding to it under the mapping α, then we say that α is *onto*, or that $\mathfrak{W}$ is mapped *onto* $\mathfrak{W}'$ by α. A mapping of the set $\mathfrak{W}$ into the set $\mathfrak{W}'$ is called *one-one* if no element of $\mathfrak{W}'$ has more than one member of $\mathfrak{W}$ to which it corresponds.

Thus, under a one-one mapping of $\mathfrak{W}$ *onto* $\mathfrak{W}'$:

1. every element of $\mathfrak{W}$ corresponds to some definite element of $\mathfrak{W}'$;

2. distinct elements of $\mathfrak{W}$ correspond to distinct elements of $\mathfrak{W}'$ (or, in other words, no two elements of $\mathfrak{W}$ have the same image);

3. every element of $\mathfrak{W}'$ has an element of $\mathfrak{W}$ corresponding to it.

Given a one-one mapping of $\mathfrak{W}$ onto $\mathfrak{W}'$ it is natural to define the *inverse* mapping of $\mathfrak{W}'$ onto $\mathfrak{W}$, under which each point M' of $\mathfrak{W}'$ is made to correspond with its (unique) inverse image M in $\mathfrak{W}$; this is a well-defined mapping (since α is one-one), and it is defined on all of $\mathfrak{W}'$ (since α is onto). It is easy to see that the inverse mapping is also one-one and onto, and that *its* inverse is precisely α.

A one-one mapping of a set onto itself, that is, a mapping of a set $\mathfrak{W}$ onto precisely the set $\mathfrak{W}$, is called a *transformation* of $\mathfrak{W}$.

In this book we shall mainly be concerned with various transformations of the plane and the mappings of plane figures induced by them.

Example 1. We make correspond to each point M of the plane its reflection in the line l (Fig. 2). Under this transformation every point M of the plane has an image: namely, the point M' symmetrically opposite M with respect to the line l. Each point P of the line l coincides with its image P'. Finally, every point M' of the plane has for its inverse image the point M which lies symmetrically opposite it with respect to l. A reflection in a line is thus a one-one mapping of the plane onto itself, that is, a transformation of the plane. A reflection is its own inverse.

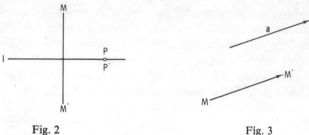

Fig. 2   Fig. 3

Example 2. We make correspond to each point M of the plane the point M' of the same plane such that the vector $\overrightarrow{MM'}$ is equal to some given vector **a**.[1] This correspondence is called a *translation*: every point M of the plane has an image M' obtained by moving a given distance in a given direction. Every point M' has a unique inverse image, which we obtain by moving an equal distance in the opposite direction (Fig. 3).

Thus a translation is a one-one mapping of the plane onto itself, that is, a transformation of the plane. The inverse transformation is the translation which moves each point an equal distance in the opposite direction.

Example 3. Suppose we are given a rectangular system of coordinates xOy in the plane. Let M be a point of the plane other than the origin O. Let r and θ be its polar coordinates. We make correspond to $M(r, \theta)$, the point $M'(r, 2\theta)$, that is, the point whose distance from O is the same as that of M and such that the angle between the rays Ox and OM' is twice the angle between

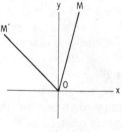

Fig. 4

---

[1] Two vectors $\overrightarrow{AB}$ and $\overrightarrow{CD}$ not lying on the same straight line are said to be equal if $ABDC$ is a parallelogram. Two vectors $\overrightarrow{AB}$ and $\overrightarrow{CD}$ lying on the same line are said to be equal if they are each equal (according to the earlier definition) to some vector $\overrightarrow{EF}$ not lying on the line. It may be proved that if $\overrightarrow{AB} = \overrightarrow{CD}$ and $\overrightarrow{CD} = \overrightarrow{EF}$, then $\overrightarrow{AB} = \overrightarrow{EF}$, so that the idea of equality of vectors has all the properties we would naturally require of it. Intuitively we may say two vectors are equal if they have the same length and if they point in the same direction.

the rays Ox and OM (Fig. 4). We make O correspond with itself. Then the correspondence we have constructed is a mapping of the plane into itself. Each point M of the plane has a unique image M', and each point $M'(r, \theta)$ has *two* inverse images: $M_1(r, \theta/2)$ and $M_2(r, \theta/2 + \pi)$ (except only O, which has the single inverse image O). Thus the mapping is onto, but it is not one-one and therefore is not a transformation.

Example 4.   Consider a hemispherical bowl touching a plane π so that its rim lies in a plane parallel to π. To each point M of π we make correspond the point M' of π which lies vertically beneath the point P of intersection of OM and the bowl, where O is the center of the hemisphere (Fig. 5). This correspondence is a mapping of the plane into itself. Every point M has its image M' lying inside the circle C whose circumference is the vertical projection onto π of the rim of the hemisphere.

Every point M' lying inside this circle C has a unique inverse image M, but no point M' lying outside or on the circumference of C has an inverse image. Thus our mapping is not a transformation of the plane but a one-one mapping of the whole plane onto the interior of C.

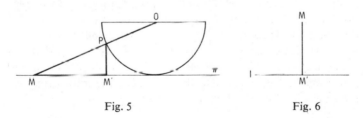

Fig. 5   Fig. 6

Example 5.   We make correspond to each point M of the plane its orthogonal projection M' on a given line l (Fig. 6). This correspondence is a mapping of the plane into itself. But whereas each point M has a unique image M' lying on l, each point M' of l has infinitely many inverse images: all those points that lie on the perpendicular line through M' to l. On the other hand, the points of the plane that do not lie on l have no inverse images at all. Thus the mapping is neither one-one onto and is certainly not a transformation of the plane.

3. Groups of Transformations

In a number of questions of geometry it is necessary to apply not one but several transformations successively. Especially important is the case where we consider a collections of transformations such that the effect of applying any finite number of these transformations successively is always the same as applying one other transformation of the collection and such that the inverse of a transformation of the collection is also in the collection. A collection satisfying these conditions is called a *group of transformations*, a concept that will be very important throughout this book. By considering groups of transformations, we may isolate a number of geometric properties that do not alter under these transformations and are characteristic of a certain branch of geometry. A knowledge of the properties invariant under the application of transformations of some group will often allow us to simplify the solution of concrete geometric problems.

Definition.   Suppose we are given any two transformations α and β defined on a set $\mathfrak{W}$. Let us carry out these transformations in succession. Let M' be the image of M under α and M'' the image of M' under β. Let γ be the correspondence under which M'' is associated with M. Then it is easy to see that γ is a one-one map of $\mathfrak{W}$ onto itself, that is, a transformation of $\mathfrak{W}$. This transformation is called the *product* of the transformation β by the transformation α, and is written $\beta\alpha$.

Thus if
$$\alpha(M) = M', \qquad \beta(M') = M'',$$
then by definition
$$(\beta\alpha)(M) = \beta(\alpha(M)) = \beta(M') = M''.$$

Let us note that, in general, $\alpha\beta \neq \beta\alpha$, that is, these two products are, in general, distinct transformations.

Example 1.   Let α be the reflection of the plane in a line l and β the translation of the plane through a distance equal to the length of the vector $\overrightarrow{PQ}$ and in the direction of $\overrightarrow{PQ}$, which is perpendicular to l. It is clear from Fig. 7 that if we first carry M a distance PQ vertically and then reflect the point N_1 so obtained in l, we obtain the point M_1 as the image of M:

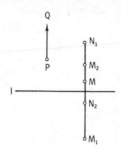

$$M_1 = (\alpha\beta)(M).$$

If we carry out the transformations α and β in the opposite order, we go first to N_2 and then to M_2:

$$M_2 = (\beta\alpha)(M),$$

Fig. 7

and it is clear that $M_2 \neq M_1$. Thus in this case $\alpha\beta \neq \beta\alpha$, for two transformations of the same set are defined to be equal only if their effect on *every* element of the set is the same, and $\beta\alpha$ and $\alpha\beta$ differ in their effect on M [as a matter of fact, for *no* point R of the plane is it true that $(\alpha\beta)(R) = (\beta\alpha)(R)$].

Example 2. Let α and β be two translations. Then $\alpha\beta = \beta\alpha$ (Fig. 8). Here for *any* point M, $\alpha\beta$ takes M to M' via M_1, and $\beta\alpha$ takes M to M' via M_2. So $\alpha\beta$ and $\beta\alpha$ have the same effect on every point and are equal.

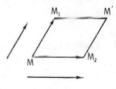

Fig. 8

Definition. That transformation of a set $\mathfrak{W}$ in which every element of $\mathfrak{W}$ is put into correspondence with itself is called the *identity transformation*.

For any $\mathfrak{W}$ we shall write the identity transformation ε. If α is any transformation of $\mathfrak{W}$ (one-one mapping of $\mathfrak{W}$ onto itself), then it is clear from the definition of the product of two transformations that

$$\alpha\varepsilon = \varepsilon\alpha = \alpha.$$

Next, if α is a transformation of M, then, as we have already seen, we can define an inverse mapping in which the image of each point is its inverse image under α; we have seen that the inverse mapping is a transformation, and we now call it the *inverse of* α and write it α^{-1}. It is clear that

$$\alpha\alpha^{-1} = \alpha^{-1}\alpha = \varepsilon$$

and that $(\alpha^{-1})^{-1} = \alpha$.

Finally, we show that *multiplication of transformations is associative*, that is, for any three transformations α, β, γ of $\mathfrak{W}$ we always have $\gamma(\beta\alpha) = (\gamma\beta)\alpha$. Let M be any element of $\mathfrak{W}$, M' its image under α, M'' the image of M' under β, and M''' the image of M'' under γ. Then, by the definition of the product of two transformations, $\beta\alpha$ will carry M into M'', and also $\gamma\beta$ will take M' into M'''. So (again by the definition of a product)

$$(\gamma(\beta\alpha))(M) = \gamma(M'') = M''',$$

and

$$((\gamma\beta)\alpha)(M) = (\gamma\beta)(M') = M'''.$$

So, by the definition of equality, we have

$$\gamma(\beta\alpha) = (\gamma\beta)\alpha.$$

Definition. A set Γ, whose elements are transformations α, β, γ, ..., all defined on the same set $\mathfrak{W}$, is called a *group* (of transformations) provided it contains together with any two transformations α, β of the set Γ their product $\alpha\beta$, and together with any transformation α of Γ its inverse α^{-1}.

We also require that Γ have at least one member. Then it is easy to see that a group of transformations always contains the identity transformation ε.

Example 3. The set of all translations of the plane (see Example 2 above) is a group.

For suppose α and β are two translations defined by the vectors **a**, **b** respectively; this means that β carries each point M of the plane into the point M' for which $\overrightarrow{MM'} = \mathbf{a}$, and β carries each point M' of the plane into the point M'' for which $\overrightarrow{M'M''} = \mathbf{b}$. The product transformation $\beta\alpha$ carries the point M into the point M'', for each point M of the plane (by the definition of the product of two transformations). By the definition of the sum of two vectors $\overrightarrow{MM''} = \overrightarrow{MM'} + \overrightarrow{M'M''} = \mathbf{a} + \mathbf{b} = \mathbf{c}$, say (Fig. 9), so that $MM'' = \mathbf{c}$ for any point M of the plane (in elementary vector algebra it may easily be shown that we obtain the same vector $\mathbf{c}$ whatever point M we start from). We have seen that the product transformation $\beta\alpha$ is also a translation, defined by the vector $\mathbf{c} = \mathbf{a} + \mathbf{b}$.

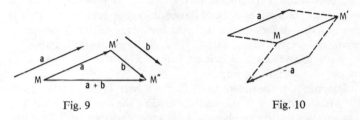

Fig. 9   Fig. 10

Next, the transformation inverse to a given translation α defined by the vector $\mathbf{a}$ is again a translation, defined by the vector $-\mathbf{a}$. (Fig. 10). The identity translation is the translation through a distance 0 (and for this translation we do not specify a direction).

We see that the set of all plane translations forms a group, which we call the translation group of the plane. This group is infinite, that is, contains infinitely many elements. It is also commutative; that is, for any two members α, β, we have $\alpha\beta = \beta\alpha$ (see Example 2 above).

Example 4. Let α be the reflection of the plane in a line l (see Example 1 of Section 2). Let Γ consist of the two elements α and ε (the identity transformation). Then Γ is a group of transformations of the plane. For if we apply the reflection twice, every point of the plane returns to its original position:

$$\alpha\alpha = \varepsilon.$$

Also

$$\alpha\varepsilon = \varepsilon\alpha = \alpha,$$

and

$$\varepsilon\varepsilon = \varepsilon.$$

So the product of any two of the transformations is again one of them, and each of the two transformations is its own inverse:

$$\alpha^{-1} = \alpha; \qquad \varepsilon^{-1} = \varepsilon.$$

(for *any* group, it is true that ε is its own inverse).

So we see that Γ is a group. It contains only two elements, and it is commutative.

Example 5. We saw in Example 3 that the set Γ of all translations of the plane forms a group. Consider the subset Γ_1 of all the translations in the direction of a fixed line (say, the x axis), both forwards and backwards. Then this set forms a group. For we may associate with each translation α the distance it carries each point. If α is associated with a (where a is a real number, positive, negative, or zero), and β is associated with b, then $\alpha\beta$ and $\beta\alpha$ are both associated with $a+b$, and α^{-1} is associated with $-a$. Just as for Γ, Γ_1 is an infinite commutative group.

Suppose now we isolate from Γ_1 the subset Γ_2 of translations in the *positive* direction of the x axis (including the identity translation). The product of two members of Γ_2 is again a member (for Γ_2 is just the set of translations associated with nonnegative real numbers, and the sum of two such is again nonnegative), but the inverse of a member (except ε) is not a member, since it is a translation in the negative direction of the x axis. So the set Γ_2 is not a group.

Example 6. Let the set B consist of all the reflections of the plane in vertical lines. If α is such a reflection in the line $x = a$, we associate α with the real number a. We add to B the identity transformation. Then the inverse of every member of B is again a member of B (in fact every member of B is its own inverse). However, suppose α and β are members of B associated with a and b respectively. Then, denoting by $M(x, y)$ the point M whose coordinates in the plane are (x, y), α carries a point $M(x, y)$ into the point $M'(2a - x, y)$, and β carries M' into the point $M''(2b - (2a - x), y) = M''(x + (2b - 2a), y)$, which is not of the form $(2c - x, y)$ for any real number c. So the product of two reflections is not a reflection at all, and B is not a group.

Note, however, that $\beta\alpha$ carries each point M of the plane a distance $(2b - 2a)$ to the right. So $\beta\alpha$ is a horizontal translation, and is, in fact, that member of Γ_1 (see Example 5) which is associated with the real number $2b - 2a$. So we are led to consider:

Example 7. Let D consist of all those transformations of the plane which belong to either B (Example 6) or Γ_1 (Example 5). We shall see that D is a group. First, we already know that the inverse of any element of B is in B and that the inverse of any element of Γ_1 is in Γ_1. So the inverse of an element of D is in D. Suppose α and β are elements of D. Then if they are both members of Γ_1 or both members of B, their product $\alpha\beta$ is in Γ_1 and therefore is in D. If β is in Γ_1 and α is in B, then suppose β is the translation associated with b and α the reflection associated with a. Then β carries $M(x, y)$ into $M'(x + b, y)$, α carries M' into $M''(2a - (x + b), y) = M''(2(a - \frac{1}{2}b) - x, y)$. So $\alpha\beta$ is the reflection associated with $a - \frac{1}{2}b$ and is in D. Finally, if β is in B, α is in Γ_1, β is the reflection associated with b, and α is the translation associated with a, it turns out that $\alpha\beta$ is the reflection associated with $b + \frac{1}{2}a$ and so is in D. Thus in every case $\alpha\beta$ is in D whenever α and β are in D, and D is a group. D is infinite but not commutative. For example, if α and β are both reflections, then $\alpha\beta$ and $\beta\alpha$ are inverse translations and not equal (unless $\alpha = \beta$) Note finally that the elements of D map the points of any horizontal line into points of the same line, so that we could consider D to be a group of transformations defined on the real line. We shall see in the next chapter that D is just the orthogonal group on the line.

Definition. Let Γ be any group of transformations. We say a subset Γ' of Γ is a *subgroup* of Γ provided that (1) the product of any two transformations of Γ' is itself in Γ'; (2) the transformation inverse to any transformation of Γ' is itself in Γ'.

In other words, Γ' is a subgroup of Γ if it is a subset which is a group in its own right.

Thus, for example, the subset Γ_0 of translations of the plane in the directions parallel to a given line is a subgroup of the group Γ of all translations in the plane (Example 2). In particular, the set Γ_1 of all horizontal translations (Example 5) is a subgroup of Γ. Γ_1 is also a subgroup of D (Example 7).

Another example of a subgroup of Γ is the set A of all those translations associated with vectors of the form $n\mathbf{a}$, where $\mathbf{a}$ is a fixed vector, and n is any integer (positive, negative, or zero). If $\mathbf{a}$ is taken parallel to the x-axis, then A is even a subgroup of Γ_1. The set of *all* transformations of the plane is itself a group, of which all the groups we have so far discussed are subgroups.

In future chapters the reader will come across further examples of subgroups of various groups of transformations.

We end this section by giving some properties of groups of transformations on any set. We leave the proofs to the reader. In the future we will use these properties without further explanation.

Let Γ be a group of transformations α, β, γ, ..., on a set $\mathfrak{W}$. Then:

(1) Γ *is right cancellative: if $\alpha\gamma = \beta\gamma$ then $\alpha = \beta$.*
(2) Γ *is left cancellative: if $\alpha\beta = \alpha\gamma$ then $\beta = \gamma$.*

In particular, if $\alpha\beta = \alpha$, then β is the identity transformation ε, and if $\beta\alpha = \alpha$, then $\beta = \varepsilon$. We will sometimes use the cancellation laws in the following manner: suppose $\sigma\rho = \sigma_1\rho_1$ and we succeed in showing that $\sigma_1 = \sigma$ (or $\rho_1 = \rho$). Then it follows that $\rho_1 = \rho$ ($\sigma_1 = \sigma$).

(3)   *Given two transformations α and β, there exists one and only one transformation γ such that $\beta = \alpha\gamma$, namely, $\gamma = \alpha^{-1}\beta$.*
(4)   *Given α and β, there exists one and only one δ such that $\beta = \delta\alpha$, namely, $\delta = \beta\alpha^{-1}$.*

CHAPTER II

Orthogonal Transformations

The concept of transformation in geometry first arose from a consideration of displacement—the movement of rigid bodies from one place to another. A characteristic of such motion, and the most important one from the point of view of geometry, is the preservation of the size and the shape of a body. Throughout its displacement, a moving body preserves its shape and dimensions and is the same at the end of the displacement as at the beginning. Thus, if we consider only the initial and final moments of the motion, we can establish a correspondence between the points of the body in its initial and in its final positions. To the point M in space occupied by a certain point P in the body at the start of the displacement we make correspond the point M' occupied by P at the end of the displacement. If M goes into M' and N into N', then the lengths of the segments MN and $M'N'$ are equal, each segment being equal to the distance between two fixed points of the rigid body. In geometry, as opposed to kinematics, a displacement is not regarded as an actual process of motion from one point to another but merely as a correspondence between the points occupied by the figure in its initial and final positions: such an approach allows us to regard displacements in geometry as mappings that take intervals into equal intervals (that is, mappings that "preserve distance"). From the geometric

point of view, such mappings are the simplest, since they preserve both the dimensions and the shapes of figures and change
only their position. We shall start our study of geometric
transformations in the plane and in space with transformations
of this type. We shall not call these transformations *displacements*, since there are distance-preserving transformations
which are not displacements (for example, reflections) but
rather *orthogonal mappings* (or *orthogonal transformations*). The
reason for the use of this terminology will appear later.
Throughout this book we shall regard mappings and transformations as defined on the whole plane or the whole of space.
Transformations and mappings of figures will be regarded as
induced by such mappings.

4. Orthogonal Mappings

Definition. *An orthogonal mapping of a plane π into a plane
π′ is a mapping under which line segments of π are carried into
equal line segments of π′.* More precisely, the mapping α of π
into π' is said to be orthogonal if, for any two points M, N of π,
the distance between M and N is equal to the distance (in π')
between $\alpha(M)$ and $\alpha(N)$. We take the notion of distance in the
plane to be fundamental.

Orthogonal mappings of π into π' are one-one and onto. For
suppose M_1 and M_2 are distinct points of π. Then their images
$M_1{}'$ and $M_2{}'$ must also be distinct, since the line segments
$M_1 M_2$ and $M_1{}'M_2{}'$ are equal. Suppose, next, M' is any point
of π'. We show that it has an inverse image M in π. Let A, B, C
be the vertices of a triangle in π, and let A', B', C' be their
respective images in π'. Then A', B', C' are the vertices of a
triangle. For otherwise B', say, would be between A' and C',
and $A'C' = A'B' + B'C'$. But then $AC = AB + BC$, which is a
contradiction, since the total length of two sides of a triangle is
always greater than the length of the third side. Since $A'B'C'$ is
a triangle, the point M' does not lie on at least one of its sides,
say the side $A'B'$. Let M'' be the reflection in $A'B'$ (perhaps

extended) of M'; then the triangles $A'B'M'$ and $A'B'M''$ are congruent. Let us construct points M_1 and M_2 in the plane π such that the triangles ABM_1 and ABM_2 are both congruent to $A'B'M'$ and $A'B'M''$. The distances from the point M_1 to A and B are M_1A and M_1B, respectively. So the image of M_1 must be the same distances from A' and B' and must therefore be either M' or M''. Similarly the image of M_2 must be either M' or M''. And since M_1 and M_2 cannot both have the image M'' (for they have distinct images), one of them has the image M'. Thus M' has an inverse image, and, in fact, a unique inverse image. Since an orthogonal mapping is one-one and onto, it has an inverse mapping, and as the inverse mapping also clearly preserves distances, the inverse of an orthogonal mapping is itself an orthogonal mapping.

Definition. An orthogonal mapping of a plane onto itself is called an orthogonal transformation of the plane.

It is clear that the product of any two orthogonal transformations is itself an orthogonal transformation, and we have already seen that the same holds for the inverse of an orthogonal transformation; it follows that the set of all orthogonal transformations of the plane forms a group, which we call the *orthogonal group* (of the plane).

In a similar way we may define orthogonal transformations of space and show that they form a group.

5. Properties of Orthogonal Mappings

Theorem I. *Under an orthogonal mapping, any three collinear points are taken into three collinear points, and any three noncollinear points are taken into three noncollinear points.*

Proof. Let P, Q, R be three collinear points, and suppose, for example, that Q lies between P and R.
Then
$$PQ + QR = PR.$$

Suppose the respective images of P, Q, R are P', Q', R'. Then by the definition of orthogonality, $P'Q' = PQ$, etc., and so

$$P'Q' + Q'R' = P'R'$$

But this is possible only if P', Q', R' lie on a line, with Q' in the middle; otherwise we should have

$$P'Q' + Q'R' > P'R'$$

Let P, Q, R be noncollinear points, and suppose their images are collinear. Then the inverse mapping which takes P' into P, etc., would take the collinear points P', Q', R' into collinear points, by what we have already proved (since the inverse of an orthogonal mapping is orthogonal). But P, Q, R are not collinear; this contradiction shows that the images are not collinear. ▼

Theorem 2. *Let α be an orthogonal map of the plane π onto the plane π'. Then the image under α of a line l in π is a line l' in π'. More precisely: given a line l in π, there is a line l' in π' such that every point of l is mapped onto some point of l', and moreover every point of l' has precisely one point of l mapped onto it. We may say more concisely that α induces a one-one mapping of l onto l'.*

Proof. Let A and B be any two distinct points of l, and let A' and B' be their (distinct) images. Let l' be the line of π' through A' and B'. Then, by Theorem 1, any point C of the line l is mapped into a point of l'. For C is collinear with A and B, so that its image must be collinear with A' and B'.

Conversely let C' be any point of l'. Then, by the same argument, its image under the inverse mapping α^{-1} of π' onto π must lie on l, so that every point of l' has an inverse image on l.

We have shown that the line l is mapped onto the line l'. That the mapping of l is one-one follows from the fact that α is one-one. ▼

As in the definitions of Section 2 (Chapter I), we call l' the image of l and l the inverse image of l' under α.

Theorem 3. *Under an orthogonal mapping α of space into itself, the image of a plane π is a plane π'. Moreover, the mapping of π onto π' is itself an orthogonal mapping.*

Proof. Let A, B, C be three noncollinear points of π, and A', B', C' their images under α. By Theorem 1, A', B', and C' are not collinear.

Let π' be the plane passing through A', B', and C'. Suppose M is an arbitrary point of π. If it lies on one of the lines BC, CA, or AB, then by Theorem 1 its image lies on $B'C'$ or $C'A'$ or $A'B'$, as the case may be. If not, suppose MA meets BC in P (Fig. 11). Then the image P' of P lies on $B'C'$ and thus lies in the plane π'. Since A, M, P are collinear, so too are their images A', M', P'. But A' and P' lie in π', so that the whole line $A'P'$ and, in particular, M' lie in π'. We have shown that the image of the plane π lies *in* the plane π'. But the inverse transformation of space must clearly map π' into π (by what we have already shown), which means in particular that α maps π *onto* π'. For every point in π' has an inverse image (an image under the inverse mapping) in π.

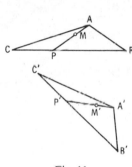

Fig. 11

That the mapping of π onto π' is one-one and orthogonal follows at once from the corresponding properties of α. ▼

Theorem 4. *Under an orthogonal mapping of a plane π onto a plane π', the image of two parallel lines of π is two parallel lines of π'.*

Proof. By Theorem 2, two parallel lines of π go into two lines of π'. If these two lines had a point in common, the inverse image of this point would be a point common to the two

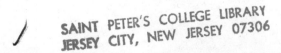

parallel lines of π, which is impossible. Thus the lines in π' have no common point; that is, they are parallel. ▼

Theorem 5.   *Under an orthogonal mapping of space:*
1.   *the image of two parallel lines is two parallel lines;*
2.   *the image of two parallel planes is two parallel planes;*
3.   *the image of a plane and a line parallel to it is a plane and a line parallel to it.*

The proofs of these propositions are left to the reader.

Theorem 6.   *Under an orthogonal mapping, the order of points on a line is preserved. That is to say, if P', R' are the images of two points P, R, then the interior points of the segment PR go into the interior points of the segment $P'R'$, while the exterior points of PR go into the exterior points of $P'R'$.*

We have already given a proof in our proof of Theorem 1.

Corollary.   *If the points P, Q lie on opposite sides of a line l, then their images P', Q' lie on opposite sides of the image l' of l.*

Let PQ meet l in R. Then R is an interior point of PQ, so that its image R' is an interior point of $P'Q'$. But R' lies on l', so that P' and Q' must lie on opposite sides of l'.

If the points P and Q lie on the same side of l, then their images lie on the same side of l'.

Theorem 7.   *Orthogonal mappings preserve angles.*

Proof.   Let a and b be two rays through a point O. Choose points A, B on a, b respectively, neither being the point O. Let O', A', B' be the images of the three points under the orthogonal mapping. Then $O'A'$, $O'B'$ will be the images of a and b respectively (by Theorem 6).

By the orthogonality of the mapping, the triangles OAB and $O'A'B'$ are congruent (three pairs of equal sides). So the respective angles are equal, and, in particular, $\angle AOB = \angle A'O'B'$. ▼

Theorem 8. *Let A, B, C be three noncollinear points of the plane π, and A', B', C' three points of the plane π' such that $B'C' = BC$, $C'A' = CA$, $A'B' = AB$. Then there exists one and only one orthogonal mapping of the plane π onto the plane π' such that the images under it of A, B, C are A', B', C', respectively.*

Proof. We construct a mapping as follows: we make A, B, C correspond to A', B', C', respectively. If P is a point of AC, we make it correspond to the point P' of $A'C'$ such that $A'P' = AP$; if P lies on the extension of AC, we let its image P' be the point on the extension of $A'C'$ such that (1) $AP = A'P'$, and (2) the points P', A', C' lie in the same order along the line $A'C'$ as do P, A, and C along the line AC.

It is easy to see that if P and P_1 are any points of AC, and P', P_1' their images, then $PP_1 = P'P_1'$ and that the order of the points P', P_1', A, C along the line $A'C'$ is the same as the order of P, P_1, A, C along the line AC. We place the points Q of AB in correspondence with the points Q' of $A'B'$ in just the same way (Fig. 12).

Suppose now that M is a point of the plane not lying on either of the lines AB or AC. We draw parallels through M to

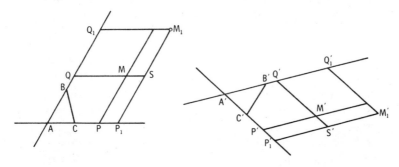

Fig. 12

meet AB and AC in Q and P, respectively. Let Q' and P' be the images of Q and P on $A'B'$ and $A'C'$. Through Q' and P' draw parallels to $A'C'$ and $A'B'$ respectively, and suppose these parallels meet in M'. Then we put M in correspondence with M'. We have now said what we put in correspondence with every point of π. Let us show that the mapping we have defined is orthogonal. Let M and M_1 be two points of π and M', M_1' their respective images. If M and M_1 both lie on AB, or both on AC, then we already know $MM_1 = M'M_1'$. If M and M_1 both lie on a line parallel to AC (say), then $MM_1 = PP_1 = P'P_1' = M'M_1'$ (where the notation is obvious). In the general case, let MQ meet M_1P_1 in S, so that $M'Q'$ meets $M_1'P_1'$ in the image S' of S (in case M, for example, lies on AB, we interpret MQ to be the line through M parallel to AC, and $Q = M$). Then $MS = PP_1 = P'P_1' = M'S'$, and $SM_1 = QQ_1 = Q'Q_1' = S'M_1'$. Next, the sides of the angles BAC and M_1SM are parallel, so that the angles must be equal or supplementary. If they are equal, then so are the angles $B'A'C'$ and $M_1'S'M'$, but if BAC and MSM_1 are supplementary, $B'A'C'$ and $M'S'M_1'$ will be too. But $\angle BAC = \angle B'A'C'$, so that $\angle MSM_1 = \angle M'S'M_1'$. Thus the triangles MSM_1 and $M'S'M_1'$ are congruent (two sides and included angle), and, in particular, $MM_1 = M'M_1'$. We have shown that the mapping we have constructed is orthogonal. ▼

   Note.   The reader should check that our proof still holds when one of M, M_1 lies on AB or AC, and even when one of them lies on one of AB, AC and the other on the other.

   We have proved that there is an orthogonal mapping of the plane π onto the plane π' in which A, B, C have A', B', C' for their images. It remains to prove that the mapping is unique. Let α be the mapping we have constructed and β any orthogonal mapping with the required properties. Then β carries any point P of AC onto a point $\beta(P)$ of $A'C'$ such that $AP = A'\beta(P)$ and $CP = C'\beta(P)$. But this means that $\beta(P) = P' = \alpha(P)$, so that α and β coincide for points of AC and similarly on AB. Suppose now M is a point of π not on AB or AC, and P and Q are defined as before. Then the image of PM under β is a line parallel to $A'B'$ (Theorem 4) and through P' (since P' is the image of P under β). Similarly, the image under β of MQ is the line through Q' parallel to $A'C'$. But these lines intersect in M', so that we must have $\beta(M) = M'$. Thus the effect of β is the same as that of α for every point of π, and so $\beta = \alpha$. We have proved the uniqueness as well as the existence of an orthogonal mapping taking A, B, C into A', B', C'.

6. Orientation

For a more detailed investigation of orthogonal transformations and the establishment of the connection between them and displacements, we shall need to introduce the important geometric concept of *orientation*. A graphic illustration of this concept is provided by a comparing two figures whose boundaries are traversed in a definite sense. Thus (Fig. 13), we say that the triangles ABC and $A'B'C'$ have the same orientation, since in both cases the vertices are traversed the same way round (clockwise). On the other hand,

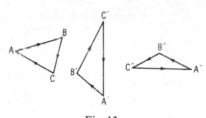

Fig. 13

the triangles ABC and $A''B''C''$ have opposite orientations.

The concept of orientation arises when we measure angles or discuss the areas of figures bounded by complicated curves (in particular, self-intersecting curves) and also in a number of questions of higher mathematics (topology). We now give a mathematical definition of orientation.

Definition I. An *oriented triangle* is an ordered triple of noncollinear points. Here the points are the vertices of the triangle, and the orientation is given by the order in which the vertices appear.

Definition 2. A *chain of triangles* joining the oriented triangle *ABC* with the oriented triangle *A'B'C'* is a finite sequence of oriented triangles, the first triangle being *ABC*, the last *A'B'C'*, such that each pairing of adjacent triangles (in the sequence) differs either by the order of the vertices alone or by one vertex which occupies the same place (first, second, or third) in each of the triangles.

Theorem I. *Any two oriented triangles ABC and A'B'C' can be joined by a chain.*

Proof. One such chain is

$$ABC, \quad ABQ, \quad APQ, \quad A'PQ, \quad A'B'Q, \quad A'B'C',$$

where *Q* is any point not on *AB* or *A'B'* and *P* is any point not on *AQ* or *A'Q* (Fig. 14). ▼

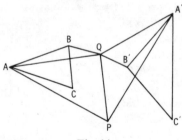

Fig. 14

Definition 3. We say two oriented triangles with the same vertices are *co-oriented* if the vertices of one of them can be obtained by a cyclic permutation of the vertices of the other. If not, we call them *anti-oriented*. (This cumbersome terminology will only be required for a couple of pages.)

Thus the triangles *ABC*, *BCA*, *CAB* are co-oriented in pairs, as are also the triangles *ACB*, *CBA*, *BAC*, while each of the latter is anti-oriented with each of the former.

Definition 4. We say two oriented triangles differing in one vertex that occupies the same position in each of them are *co-oriented* if these vertices lie on the same side of the line joining the other two vertices and otherwise *anti-oriented*. Thus if C and D lie on the same side of the line AB, the triangles ABC and ABD are co-oriented. If C and D are on opposite sides of AB, then these triangles are anti-oriented. (Fig. 15).

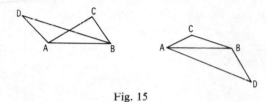

Fig. 15

Definition 5. Given two oriented triangles ABC and $A'B'C'$ and a chain joining them, we say ABC and $A'B'C'$ have the *same orientation* if the number of pairs of adjacent triangles (in the chain) that are anti-oriented is even, and otherwise we say ABC and $A'B'C'$ have *opposite orientations* (Figs. 16 and 17). In order to show that this is a meaningful definition, we need to establish:

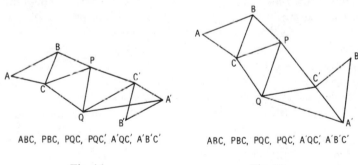

ABC, PBC, PQC, PQC; A'QC; A'B'C'   ABC, PBC, PQC, PQC; A'QC; A'B'C'

Fig. 16   Fig. 17

Theorem 2. *Given two oriented triangles ABC and $A'B'C'$, the number of pairs of adjacent triangles in a chain joining ABC to $A'B'C'$ that are anti-oriented is either always even or always odd.*

If we prove this theorem, we shall have shown that the property of two triangles of having the same or opposite orientation is independent of the choice of a chain between them.

Theorem 2 is a consequence of:

Theorem 3. Let (x_i, y_i) and (x_i', y_i') be the coordinates of the vertices of the oriented triangles ABC and A'B'C', respectively $(i = 1, 2, 3)$. In order that the triangles have the same orientation (with respect to a given chain), it is necessary and sufficient that the determinants

$$\begin{vmatrix} x_1 & y_1 & 1 \\ x_2 & y_2 & 1 \\ x_3 & y_3 & 1 \end{vmatrix} \quad \text{and} \quad \begin{vmatrix} x_1' & y_1' & 1 \\ x_2' & y_2' & 1 \\ x_3' & y_3' & 1 \end{vmatrix}$$

have the same sign.

Let us first see why this theorem entails Theorem 2. Suppose ABC and $A'B'C'$ have the same orientation with respect to a chain D. Then, by the "necessary" part of Theorem 3, the determinants (1) have the same sign. Let D' be any chain joining the triangles. Then by the "sufficient" part of Theorem 3 the triangles have the same orientation with respect to D'. We see, therefore, that if the triangles have the same orientation with respect to one chain, they have it with respect to every chain, and it follows that if they have the opposite orientation with respect to one chain, they have it with respect to every chain. So the property of pairs of oriented triangles of having the same or opposite orientations is independent of the connecting chains.

Proof. Consider a pair of adjacent triangles in the given chain joining ABC to $A'B'C'$, and suppose first that they differ in one vertex. If the triangles are MNS and MNT, we show that the determinants

$$\delta_1 = \begin{vmatrix} x_M & y_M & 1 \\ x_N & y_N & 1 \\ x_S & y_S & 1 \end{vmatrix} \quad \text{and} \quad \delta_2 = \begin{vmatrix} x_M & y_M & 1 \\ x_N & y_N & 1 \\ x_T & y_T & 1 \end{vmatrix}$$

(the notation being obvious) have the same or opposite sign, according as S and T lie on the same or opposite sides of MN.

Now the equation of the line MN is

$$\begin{vmatrix} x_M & y_M & 1 \\ x_N & y_N & 1 \\ x & y & 1 \end{vmatrix} = 0.$$

It is known from analytic geometry that S and T lie on the same side of MN if and only if the substitution of their co-ordinates in the left side of the equation for MN gives us two numbers with the same sign, that is, if and only if δ_1 and δ_2 have the same sign. Thus, by Definition 4, δ_1 and δ_2 have the same sign if and only if MNS and MNT are co-oriented.

If two adjacent triangles of the chain differ only in the order of their vertices, then the corresponding determinants (constructed as was δ_1) have the same sign if and only if the vertices of one triangle are obtained from those of the other by a cyclic permutation; that is, if and only if these triangles are co-oriented (Definition 3).

Thus the number of sign changes in the sequence of determinants corresponding to the successive triangles of our chain is equal to the number of pairs of adjacent triangles which are anti-oriented. So if the determinants (1) have the same sign, the number of sign changes in the sequence of determinants must be even, and the number of pairs of adjacent triangles which are anti-oriented must be even. Similarly, if the determinants (1) have opposite signs, then the number of sign changes, and therefore also the number of pairs of adjacent anti-oriented triangles, must be odd. This proves the theorem. ▼

Note. It follows from this theorem that co-oriented triangles have the same orientation, and anti-oriented ones opposite orientations. Therefore, we no longer need to talk of co- or anti-oriented triangles.

The concept of orientation may be extended to three-dimensional space:

Definition 6. An *oriented tetrahedron* is an ordered quadruple of points in space (the vertices) not all lying in one plane.

Definition 7. A *chain of tetrahedra* connecting an oriented tetrahedron $A = A_1 A_2 A_3 A_4$ with an oriented tetrahedron $A' A_1' A_2' A_3' A_4'$ is a finite sequence of oriented tetrahedra, the first of which is A and the last A', such that two adjacent tetrahedra of the sequence differ either only by the order of their vertices or by a single vertex occupying the same place in both of them.

It can easily be shown that any two tetrahedra can be joined by a chain.

Definition 8. We say that two oriented tetrahedra with the same vertices are *co-oriented* if the vertices of one of them can be obtained from those of the other by an even permutation.

We say that a permutation taking a sequence of elements into a different sequence of the same elements is *even* if the second sequence can be obtained from the first by an even number of transpositions of pairs of elements. It can be shown that whatever sequence of transpositions we choose in order to take one given sequence into another, we shall either always need an odd number or always an even number. A permutation in which an odd number of transpositions is required is called an *odd* permutation. For example, the permutation $\begin{pmatrix} 2 & 3 & 4 & 1 \\ 1 & 2 & 4 & 3 \end{pmatrix}$ is even, since we may go from the sequence 2341 to the sequence 1243 by means of the following two transpositions:

$$2341 \rightarrow 1342; \qquad 1342 \rightarrow 1243.$$

On the other hand, the permutation $\begin{pmatrix} 2 & 3 & 1 & 4 \\ 1 & 2 & 4 & 3 \end{pmatrix}$ is odd, since we may reach 1243 from 2314 by means of three transpositions as follows: $2314 \rightarrow 1324 \rightarrow 1234 \rightarrow 1243$. So, for example, the oriented tetrahedra $A_2A_3A_4A_1$ and $A_1A_2A_4A_3$ are co-oriented, but $A_2A_3A_1A_4$ and $A_1A_2A_4A_3$ are anti-oriented.

Definition 9. Two oriented tetrahedra differing in a single vertex that occupies the same position in each of them are said to be *co-oriented* if these vertices lie on the same side of the plane through the other three vertices, and otherwise *anti-oriented*.

Definition 10. If a chain joining the oriented tetrahedra A and A' is such that the number of pairs of adjacent tetrahedra in it that are anti-oriented is even, then A and A' are said to have the *same orientation*, and otherwise they are said to have *opposite orientations*.

This definition is justified by the following theorem, which, like Theorem 2, may be proved by a consideration of determinants:

Theorem 4. *In any two chains joining the given oriented tetrahedra A and A', the respective numbers of pairs of anti-oriented adjacent tetrahedra will be both even or both odd.*

The definition we have given of orientation in Euclidean three-dimensional space can be generalized to n-dimensional space.

7. Orthogonal Transformations of the First and Second Kinds

Theorem 1. *If a triangle ABC and its image $A'B'C'$ under an orthogonal transformation of the plane have the same orientation, then so also do any triangle and its image. Conversely, if ABC and $A'B'C'$ have opposite orientations, so also do any triangle and its image.*

Proof. Suppose the triangles ABC and $A'B'C'$ have the same orientation, and let PQR be any triangle and $P'Q'R'$ its image. We show that PQR and $P'Q'R'$ have the same orientation. We start by making the following remark: If D_1, D_2, ..., D_n is any sequence of triangles, then D_1 and D_n will have the same orientation if the number of pairs of adjacent triangles in the sequence having opposite orientation is even, and otherwise they will have opposite orientation. The proof is given by supplying a chain of triangles between each pair D_r, D_{r+1}, and we leave it to the reader. Suppose now S is a chain of triangles joining PQR to ABC. It will be mapped under the orthogonal transformation α into a chain S' joining $P'Q'R'$ and $A'B'C'$. The number of anti-oriented pairs in S' is the same as the number in S, so that $A'B'C'$ and $P'Q'R'$ will have the same orientation if and only if ABC and PQR do. On considering the sequence of triangles PQR, ABC, $A'B'C'$, $P'Q'R'$, the reader will see that in any case PQR and $P'Q'R'$ have the same orientation.

The second part may be proved analogously, but it follows from what we know already. Thus, suppose ABC and $A'B'C'$ have opposite orientations and PQR is any triangle, If PQR and $P'Q'R'$ have the same orientation, then, by what we have already proved, every triangle has the same orientation as its image; in particular, the triangle ABC. This contradiction shows that PQR and $P'Q'R'$ must have opposite orientations. ▼

Definition I. An orthogonal transformation will be said to be *of the first kind* if it preserves the orientation of every triangle. If the transformation changes the orientation of every triangle, it will be said to be *of the second kind*. Theorem 1 shows that every orthogonal transformation is either of the first or of the second kind. The classification into transformations of the first and second kind can be extended into space, and even into n-dimensional Euclidean space for any positive integer n.

Definition 2. An orthogonal transformation of the first kind is called a *displacement*.

In mechanics and physics a displacement is commonly regarded as a process in which a body moves from one position to another. During the motion, lengths of segments and sizes of angles, and also orientation, are preserved. In a number of questions in geometry we are interested only in the initial and final positions of the body. So, instead of thinking of a body that moves through space from one position to another, we think of an orthogonal transformation such that the image of a plane figure (the " body " in its initial position) is another plane figure (the body in its final position). The transformation has to be orthogonal, since we want the image to be congruent with the original figure, and it has to be of the first kind, since we wish the orientation of the image to be the same as that of the original. The set of all orthogonal transformations of the plane of the first kind is a subgroup of the full orthogonal group. For it is clear that the product of two orientation-preserving maps also preserves orientation, and so does the inverse of an orientation-preserving map.

Let us note that the product of an orthogonal transformation of the first and second kinds is of the second kind and that the product of two transformations of the second kind is of the first kind. Compare Example 7 at the end of Chapter I, where Γ_1 is the set of orthogonal transformations of the line of the first kind, B those of the second, and D the full orthogonal group of the line.

We showed above that there exists a unique orthogonal transformation carrying three given points ABC into three given points $A'B'C'$ such that the triangles ABC and $A'B'C'$ are congruent. We can now sharpen this result.

Theorem 2. *Given two distinct points A, B and two points A', B' such that A'B' = AB, there exists a unique orthogonal transformation of the first kind and a unique orthogonal transformation of the second kind (each defined on the plane) such that the images of A and B are A' and B', respectively.*

Proof. Choose an arbitrary point C not lying on the line AB, and let C' and C'' be the two points of the plane for which the triangles $A'B'C'$ and $A'B'C''$ are congruent with the triangle ABC. It is clear that any orthogonal transformation of the plane which takes A and B into A' and B' must take C into either C' or C''. Moreover, there is precisely one transformation α taking A, B, C into A', B', C', respectively, and precisely one orthogonal transformation β taking A, B, C into A', B', C'', by Theorem 8 of Section 5. Now C' and C'' lie on opposite sides of $A'B'$, so that the triangles $A'B'C'$ and $A'B'C''$, have opposite orientations. So just one of them, say $A'B'C'$, has the same orientation as ABC. But then α is of the first kind, by Theorem 1 and β is of the second. Thus, exactly one of the two possible orthogonal transformations taking A, B into A', B' is of the first kind, and one is of the second. ▼

8. The Fundamental Types of Orthogonal Transformation (Translation, Reflection, Rotation)

In this section we consider the fundamental types of orthogonal transformation, in terms of which every such transformation can be expressed.

8.1. TRANSLATION

Suppose we are given a vector **a** of the plane π. We make correspond to each point M of π the point M' for which $MM' = \mathbf{a}$ (Fig. 18). This correspondence is a transformation of the plane called a *translation*. Thus, under a translation, every point is carried a given distance in a given direction.

Translations are orthogonal transformations of the plane. For suppose M_1 and M_2 are given points and M_1', M_2' their images under the given translation (Fig. 19). Then, by the definition of a translation, $\overrightarrow{M_1M_1'} = \overrightarrow{M_2M_2'} = \mathbf{a}$. Adding to both sides the vector $\overrightarrow{M_1'M_2}$, we find that $\overrightarrow{M_1M_1'} + \overrightarrow{M_1'M_2} = \overrightarrow{M_1'M_2} + \overrightarrow{M_2M_2'}$, or $\overrightarrow{M_1M_2} = \overrightarrow{M_1'M_2'}$, so that the segments

M_1M_2 and $M_1'M_2'$ are equal (actually, we have even shown that they are parallel).

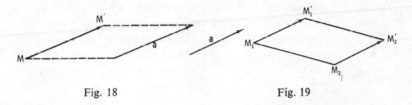

Fig. 18   Fig. 19

A translation is an orthogonal transformation of the first kind. For suppose the translation takes some point A into A', and A' into A''. Let C be any point not lying on AA', and suppose its image is C'. We show that the oriented triangles $AA'C$ and $A'A''C'$ have the same orientation. It will follow at once from Theorem 1 that the translation is a transformation of the first kind. Consider the chain of triangles:

$$AA'C, \quad C'A'C, \quad C'A'A'', \quad A'A''C'.$$

Since $ACC'A'$ is a parallelogram, A and C' lie on opposite sides of CA', so that the first pair of triangles in the chain is anti-oriented. Similarly, $A'CC'A''$ is a parallelogram, so that C and A'' lie on opposite sides of $C'A'$, and the second pair in the chain is anti-oriented. Finally, the last pair is related by a cyclic permutation and so is co-oriented. Thus in the chain there are two changes of orientation, and therefore $AA'C$ and its image $A'A''C$ have the same orientation.

Let us note that any transformation of the plane in which vectors are transformed into equal vectors is a translation. For (with the obvious notation) if $\overrightarrow{M_1M_2} = \overrightarrow{M_1'M_2'}$ it follows that $\overrightarrow{M_1M_2} + \overrightarrow{M_2M_1'} = \overrightarrow{M_2M_1'} + \overrightarrow{M_1'M_2'}$ so that $\overrightarrow{M_1M_1'} = \overrightarrow{M_2M_2'} = \mathbf{a}$, where $\mathbf{a}$ is a constant vector not depending on our choice of M.

We have already seen (Example 3 at the end of Chapter I) that the set of all translations (including the identity transformation) is a group.

8.2. Reflection in a Line

Suppose in the plane we are given a line *l*. Let us make correspond to each point *M* of the plane its reflection *M'* in *l* (we say *M'* is the reflection of *M* in *l* if *l* is the perpendicular bisector of the segment *MM'*). We make the points of *l* correspond to themselves. This correspondence is called a reflection (Fig. 20).

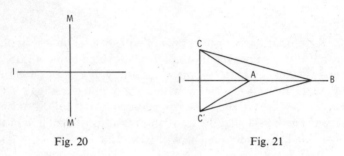

Fig. 20   Fig. 21

A reflection is an orthogonal transformation of the second kind. It is clear that lengths are not altered by a reflection, so that it is an orthogonal transformation. To show it is of the second kind, let *A* and *B* be two points of *l* and *C* a point not on *l*. Let *C'* be the reflection of *C* in *l* (Fig. 21). Then the triangle *ABC* is mapped by the reflection into the triangle *ABC'*. These two triangles are anti-oriented by definition, so that they have opposite orientations (consider the chain whose only two members are *ABC*, *ABC'*). So, by Theorem 1, Section 7, the reflection changes the orientation of *every* triangle and thus is of the second kind.

A reflection may be defined as the unique transformation, other than the identity, that leaves fixed at least two given points.

Suppose we are given that the transformation α leaves fixed the points *A* and *B*. We already know of two transformations that leave *A* and *B* fixed: the identity and the reflection in the line *AB*. By Theorem 2, Section 7, these are the only two, and since α is not the identity by hypothesis, it must be the reflection.

8.3. REFLECTION IN A POINT

Suppose we are given a point O of the plane. Let us make correspond to each point M of the plane the point M' symmetrically opposite it with respect to O. That is, M' is that point of the plane for which O is the midpoint of MM'. We make O correspond to itself. The transformation we have defined is called the *reflection in O*. We show that reflection in O is an orthogonal transformation of the first kind. Let A', B' be the images under the reflection of two given points A, B, respectively. Then, if A, B, O are not collinear, the triangles AOB and $A'OB'$ are congruent (two sides and included angle), so that $A'B' = AB$. We leave the case where A, B, O are collinear to the reader. This shows that reflection is an orthogonal transformation. To see that it is of the first kind, choose A and B not collinear with O and consider the sequence

$$AOB, \quad A'OB, \quad A'OB'.$$

The triangles AOB and $A'OB$ have opposite orientation, since A and A' are on opposite sides of OB; and $A'OB$ and $A'OB'$ have opposite orientation, since B and B' are on opposite sides of OA'. So AOB and $A'OB'$ have the same orientation, and the transformation is of the first kind.

Under a reflection in a point, each segment is transformed into an equal segment having the opposite direction: strictly speaking, $\overrightarrow{A'B'} = -\overrightarrow{AB}$, for every pair of points A, B. If A and B are collinear with O, then $A'B'$ is collinear with AB, and otherwise it is parallel (but pointing the other way).

Conversely, it is true that any transformation of the plane in which vectors are taken into their negatives is a reflection in a point.

For it is first clear that the transformation is orthogonal. It is not the identity, so choose a point A whose image A' is distinct from it. Let O be the midpoint of AA' and M any point not on the line AA'. We show that the image M' of M is its reflection in O. We know that $\overrightarrow{AM} = -\overrightarrow{A'M'} = \overrightarrow{M'A'}$, so that $AMA'M'$ form the vertices of a parallelogram. Its diagonals bisect each other in O, so that O is the midpoint of MM'. The proof that the image of a point on AA' is its reflection in O is left to the reader.

8.4. ROTATION

Suppose that we fix in the plane a point O. We wish to define the transformation consisting of a rotation about O through a given angle. The reader will probably have a fairly clear idea without any explanation what such a transformation should be. We need to give a rigorous definition, which is best done by first considering the concept of an *oriented angle*.

Let S be the circle with center O and radius 1. If M and N are any points on S, the ordinary angle $\angle MON$ may be defined as the pair of rays (OM, ON) and its (radian) measure as the shorter distance between M and N measured around S.

For our purposes, this notion is inadequate. We wish to distinguish between the rotation about O that carries M into N and the rotation that carries N into M. We shall thus need to distinguish between the angle $\angle MON$ (the angle from M to N) and $\angle NOM$ (the angle from N to M). The distinction is exactly parallel to the one we must make for translations; we need to distinguish between the translation that carries M into N (translation through the vector $\overrightarrow{MN}$), and that which carries N into M (translation through the vector $\overrightarrow{NM}$). The concept corresponding to "line segment MN" here is "ordinary angle $\angle MON$," and the concept corresponding to "vector $\overrightarrow{MN}$" will be "oriented angle $\angle MON$."

The formal definition of an oriented angle is quite easy: it is an *ordered* pair of rays OM and ON from a given origin O. This definition is exactly similar to the definition of a vector or a directed line segment as an ordered pair of points. Thus the notation we should perhaps use is (OM, ON), where we take note of the order; this angle is to be considered distinct from (ON, OM).) However, it is usual in practice to use the same notation as for an unoriented angle. Of course, we still have to take note of the order; $\angle MON$ is different from $\angle NOM$.

We define the oriented angles $\angle MON$ and $\angle M'O'N'$ to be *equal* provided there is an orthogonal transformation *of the first kind* carrying OM onto $O'M'$ and ON onto $O'N'$. An equivalent definition is as follows. Since M and N are only used to indicate the two rays, we may as well take $OM = 1 = ON$ and $O'M' = 1 = O'N'$. Then the oriented angles $\angle MON$ and $\angle M'O'N'$ are equal if and only if the triangles MON and $M'O'N'$ are congruent *and have the same orientation*.

Our next task is to define the measure of an oriented angle $\angle MON$, just as we would have to define lengths if we were talking about segments. We start by defining a counterclockwise arc from M to N (we are assuming as before that M and N both lie on the circle S with center O). We fix an oriented triangle ABC in the plane. Then a certain one of the arcs from M to N will be said to be the counterclockwise arc if the triangle MPN has the same orientation as the triangle ABC, where P is some point of the arc we are considering. Of course, we must verify that this gives us an unambiguous answer. Verification follows from the facts that if P and Q lie on the same one of the arcs from M to N, the oriented triangles MPN and MQN will have the same orientation, whereas if they lie on opposite arcs, these triangles will have

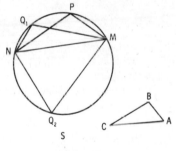

Fig. 22

opposite orientations (Fig. 22). To make this definition accord with our usual idea of what "counterclockwise arc" should mean, we merely have to choose the orientation of triangle ABC suitably. Our choice does not make any difference to the mathematics involved—all it affects is the appropriateness of our terminology. Of course, once we have chosen our triangle, we must remain with our choice.

We now define the measure of the oriented angle $\angle MON$ to be the length α of the counterclockwise arc from M to N. To ensure that this definition is respectable, we must check that equal angles have the same measure. But this is obvious. We shall write $\angle MON = \alpha$ to mean that the angle $\angle MON$ has measure α.

We next define the sum of two oriented angles. We define $\angle MON + \angle N'O'P'$ to be the angle $\angle MOP$, where $\angle NOP = \angle N'O'P'$. That is, we construct an angle $\angle NOP$ with initial ray ON, and equal to the angle $\angle N'O'P'$ (Fig. 23). We may

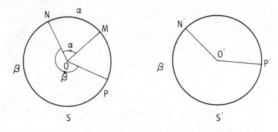

Fig. 23

easily verify that the sums of angles equal in pairs are themselves equal (according to our definition of equality of oriented angles). We must now establish the connection between the sum of two angles (an angle) and the sum of their measures (a number). A little thought will convince the reader that what we would like to say is: if $\angle AOC = \alpha$ and $\angle B'O'D' = \beta$, then their sum $\angle AOC + \angle B'O'D'$ has measure $\alpha + \beta$. After all, we can make exactly corresponding assertion about line segments, and it is just this correspondence between numbers and segments (congruent segments have equal lengths, and the sum of two segments has length equal to the sum—different meaning of sum!—of the lengths of its components) that makes numbers relevant to calculations with lengths.

In our case, however, this equivalence will not work completely. For the measure of an oriented angle is the length of an arc of the unit circle and thus is a number lying between 0 and 2π. Yet $\alpha + \beta$ in the assertion above might be greater than 2π (Fig. 24).

Intuitively we would say there is no difficulty; a rotation counterclockwise through $2\pi + \alpha$ brings us to the same point as a rotation through α. So perhaps we might say that an oriented angle $\angle MON$ should be allowed measure α whenever a point moving counterclockwise around S through a distance α starting from M would end up at N. This would allow the point to make a number of revolutions before stopping and would

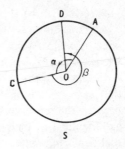

Fig. 24

also allow a number of different measures to the same angle. However, as far as a formal definition is concerned, it is somewhat difficult to capture this concept. The dynamic concept of a point moving around a circle is much more elusive than the static concept of a counterclockwise arc. So we will content ourselves with two possible formulations that can be made rigorous, and the reader (and author!) need not stop thinking about moving points in deference to the formulations if he does not wish.

The first course is to allow an infinity of values for the measure of the angle $\angle MON$. If α is the value we have already defined (the "principal value"), we also allow all the values $\alpha + 2\pi$, $\alpha + 4\pi$, $\alpha + 6\pi$, ... It is convenient, in addition, to allow the values $\alpha - 2\pi$, $\alpha - 4\pi$, ... Intuitively, these would correspond to the idea of a point reaching N from M by going so many revolutions clockwise after first going α counterclockwise.

The second course is to perform all our arithmetic with the measure of oriented angles not in the real numbers, but in the real numbers "modulo 2π." Since we are concerned only with addition of angles, we are working in the additive group of real numbers modulo 2π. It is a group because every element has an additive inverse; the inverse of α is $2\pi - \alpha$, since the sum of these is 2π, which we agree to identify with 0. There is no difficulty in a corresponding definition of subtraction for angles; we may define $-\angle MON = \angle NOM$, and then define $\angle AOC$

$- \angle B'O'D'$ to be the same as $\angle AOC + (-\angle B'O'D')$ (Fig. 25).

The question of which definition to adopt is one of convenience. If we are working, for example, with a problem concerning lengths of cable unrolling from a drum, the first definition is the more appropriate. If we are working with rotations of the plane, as we will be, the second is the more appropriate, because the rotation through α and the rotation through $2\pi + \alpha$ are identical in their effect on the plane, even if they are not identical on a spool of thread.

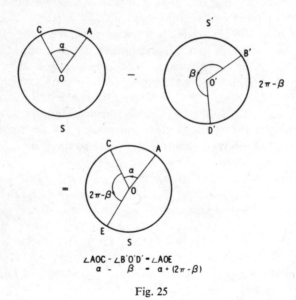

$$\angle AOC - \angle B'O'D' = \angle AOE$$
$$\alpha \quad - \quad \beta \quad = \quad \alpha + (2\pi - \beta)$$

Fig. 25

Whichever course we adopt, we can now safely say that if $\angle AOC = \alpha$ and $\angle B'O'D' = \beta$, then $\angle AOC + \angle B'O'D' = \alpha + \beta$. In the first case this says that if α is one of the measures of the angle $\angle AOC$ and β is one of the measures of $\angle B'O'D'$, then $\alpha + \beta$ (the ordinary sum of the ordinary signed numbers) is one of the measures of the sum angle $\angle AOC + \angle B'O'D'$ (constructed according to the definition we gave earlier).

In the second case this says that if α is *the* measure of the angle $\angle AOC$ and β is *the* measure of the angle $\angle B'O'D'$, then $\alpha + \beta$ is *the* measure of the sum angle. However, in this case, α and β are not strictly real numbers, but elements of the group of real numbers modulo 2π, and $\alpha + \beta$ is the result of performing the operation of addition *as defined in this group*. If we represent α and β as real numbers lying between 0 and 2π, then their sum will be represented either as $\alpha + \beta$ (the ordinary sum) or $\alpha + \beta - 2\pi$. For example, $\pi/4 + \pi/2 = 3\pi/4$, but $\pi/4 + 3\pi/4 = 0$, $\pi/2 + 3\pi/4 = \pi/4$.

We are now in a position to define a rotation. Given the *center of rotation* O, and an oriented angle $\angle AOC = \alpha$, the *angle of rotation*, we make correspond to each point M of the plane the point M' for which $OM = OM'$ and the oriented angle $\angle MOM' = \alpha$. Of course, $O' = O$.

A rotation about O is completely defined by its effect on a single point $M \neq O$. For if the image of M is M', then the rotation is the one through the angle $\alpha = \angle MOM'$.

A rotation is an orthogonal transformation of the first kind. For given M and N, let the oriented angle $\angle MON$ have measure θ (principal value). Then

$$\angle M'ON' = \angle M'OM + \angle MON + \angle NON'$$

$$= -\alpha + \theta + \alpha$$

$$= \theta.$$

We examine what this sequence of equalities says. The first line asserts the equality (according to our definition of equality of oriented angles) of the left-hand angle and the sum angle of the three angles on the right. Actually the two are not merely equal; they are identical. We have already discussed the step from the first equality to the second. The last step is purely algebraic. In the first interpretation, it is an equality in the additive group of reals; in the second, it is an equality in the additive group of reals mod 2π.

We have thus shown that the triangles MON and $M'ON'$ have the same principal value for their oriented angle at O. But then they also have the same ordinary angle at O. It will be

θ if $O \le \theta \le \pi$, and $2\pi - \theta$ otherwise. Now $OM = OM'$ and $ON = ON'$, by definition of the rotation. So the triangles are

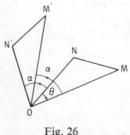

Fig. 26

congruent (side, angle, side). We do not exclude the case where M, O, and N are collinear ($\theta = 0$ or π); the congruence still follows. A reference to our original definition of equality of oriented angles shows more; the two angles have the same orientation. We have thus proved our assertion (Fig. 26).

9. Representations of Orthogonal Transformations as Products of the Fundamental Orthogonal Transformations: Translations, Reflections, and Rotations

We have examined three special types of orthogonal transformation: translation, reflection, and rotation. In this section we shall show that any plane orthogonal transformation may be represented as a product of such special transformations.

Theorem I. *Any (plane) orthogonal transformation of the first kind is either a translation or a rotation (including the possibility of a rotation through π, that is, reflection in a point).*

Proof. Let A be any point of the plane, B its image under the transformation α, and C the image of B under α.

There are three possible cases to consider:

Case I. The line segments AB and BC lie on the same line and point the same way (Fig. 27). In this case, the translation by the vector $\overrightarrow{AB}$ ($= \overrightarrow{BC}$) has the same effect on A and B as does α. So by Theorem 2 of Section 7, α, in fact, *is* this translation.

Case 2. The line segments AB and BC lie on the same line but point in opposite directions. In this case, the points C and A coincide (Fig. 28).

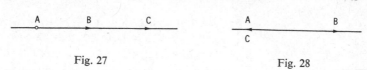

Fig. 27   Fig. 28

α takes A into B and B into A, but so too does the reflection in the midpoint O of AB. Since the reflection too is a transformation of the first kind, again by Theorem 2 (Section 7), α must be this reflection.

Case 3. The line segments AB and BC do not lie on the same line (Fig. 29). Let O be the point of intersection of the perpendicular bisectors to AB and BC. Then $AO = BO = CO$, so that the triangles ABO, BCO are congruent. But then the rotation β about O that carries A into B also carries B into C, so that by the usual argument $\beta = \alpha$, and α is a rotation. ▼

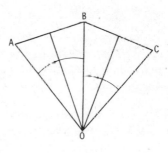

Fig. 29

Note. If in the plane we are given two equal line segments AB and $A'B'$, then we may give a direct description of the orthogonal transformation of the first kind that takes A into A' and B into B'. For, if AB and $A'B'$ are parallel and point in the same direction, the transformation is the translation through $\overrightarrow{AA'} = \overrightarrow{BB'}$. If AB and $A'B'$ are parallel but point in opposite directions, the transformation is the reflection in the midpoint O of AA' (or BB'). (These assertions remain true even when AB and $A'B'$ are collinear.) Suppose now AB and $A'B'$ are not parallel. We know (Theorem 2 of Section 7) that there exists a unique transformation of the first kind taking A to A' and B to B'. Now this transformation cannot be either a translation or a reflection in a point (since this would take the line segment AB into a parallel line segment); it must therefore be a rotation.

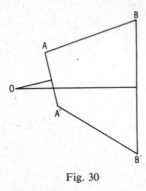

Fig. 30

If the center of this rotation is O, then $OA = OA'$, so that O lies on the perpendicular bisector of AA', and similarly O lies on the perpendicular bisector of BB'. Thus O is the point of intersection of these (nonparallel!) lines. The reader should give a direct proof for himself that the rotation about O that takes A into A' will also take B into B' (Fig. 30).

Theorem 2. *Any plane orthogonal transformation α of the second kind can be represented uniquely as the product of a reflection σ in some line l and a translation τ parallel to l. The line l is uniquely defined by α, and $\sigma\tau = \tau\sigma$.*

Proof. We distinguish the same three cases as we did for Theorem 1. Let B be the image of the point A under α, and let C be the image of B.

Case I. AB and BC lie on the same line and point the same way (Fig. 31). Let τ be the translation determined by the vector $\overrightarrow{AB} (= \overrightarrow{BC})$ and σ the reflection in the line AB.

Then $\beta = \sigma\tau = \tau\sigma$, like α, carries A into B and B into C. Since α and β are both of the second kind, Theorem 2 (Section 7) shows that they are the same.

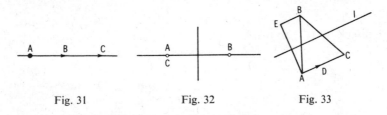

Fig. 31   Fig. 32   Fig. 33

Case 2. C coincides with A (Fig. 32). Then α is, by the familiar argument, the reflection σ in the perpendicular bisector of AB.

In this case we take τ to be the identity translation, and have $\sigma\tau = \tau\sigma = \sigma$.

Case 3. AB and BC do not lie on the same line (Fig. 33).

Let l be the line through the midpoints of AB and BC, and let D be the midpoint of AC. Let σ be the reflection in l and τ the translation along $\overrightarrow{AD} = \overrightarrow{DC}$. Then σ takes A to E, and τ takes E to B, so that $\tau\sigma$ takes A to B. Similarly, σ takes B to D, and τ takes D to C, so that $\tau\sigma$ takes B to C. By the usual argument, $\alpha = \tau\sigma$. It is easily checked that $\sigma\tau = \tau\sigma$.

We now show that such a representation of α is unique. Suppose $\alpha = \sigma\tau$, where τ is not the identity. Then l is the only line mapped into itself by α. For if m meets l in P, its image m' meets l in $P' \neq P$ (Fig. 34), so that $m' \neq m$. If n is parallel to l then $n' \neq n$ (Fig. 35).

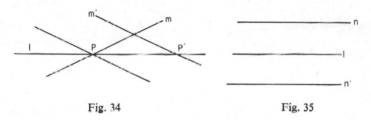

Fig. 34 Fig. 35

Suppose now that $\alpha = \sigma'\tau'$, where σ' and τ' have axis l'. By what we have proved, $l' = l$ (since l' is invariant under α). Thus $\sigma' = \sigma$, and, by cancellation (end of Chapter I), $\tau' = \tau$.

We have shown that if α has one representation $\alpha = \sigma\tau$, where $\tau \neq \varepsilon$, then the representation is unique. The only remaining possibility is that for *every* representation, $\tau = \varepsilon$, But then $\alpha = \sigma$ has the unique representation $\sigma\varepsilon$. ▼

Theorem 3. *Any orthogonal transformation of the first kind may be represented as the product of two reflections in lines; any orthogonal transformation of the second kind either is itself a reflection in a line or can be represented as the product of three such reflections.*

Proof. Let α be an orthogonal transformation of the first kind. Then, by Theorem 1, it is either a rotation or a translation or a reflection in a point.

(1) Suppose first that α is a translation, and that $\alpha(A) = A'$ (Fig. 36). Let l_1 be the perpendicular bisector of AA' and l_2 the perpendicular to AA' through A'. Let σ_1 and σ_2 be the reflections in these two lines, respectively.

Under the transformation $\sigma_2\sigma_1$, the point A will go into A', and any point B such that AB is parallel to l_1 will go into the same point B' as it would under the transformation α. So, by the usual argument, $\alpha = \sigma_2\sigma_1$.

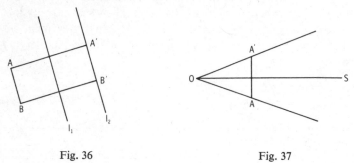

Fig. 36   Fig. 37

(2) Suppose now that α is a rotation. Let O be its center and A' the image of some point A (Fig. 37). Let OS be the perpendicular bisector of AA' and σ_1 and σ_2 the reflections in OS and OA', respectively. Then, under $\sigma_2\sigma_1$, O remains in place, and A is taken to A'. So, by the usual argument, $\alpha = \sigma_2\sigma_1$.

The reader should check that this construction works also for a reflection in O; in this case, OS will be perpendicular to AOA'.

Suppose now that α is an orthogonal transformation of the second kind. Then either it is itself a reflection or it can be represented as the product of a reflection and a translation (this is part of the content of Theorem 2). But a translation can itself be represented as the product of two reflections, as we have just seen. So α can be represented as the product of three reflections. ▼

Note that the representation of an orthogonal transformation as a product of reflections is not unique. For transformations of the first kind, we make the situation clear in Theorem 4; for transformations of the second kind, the situation is more complicated.

Theorem 4. *Consider the translation* $\tau = \sigma_2 \sigma_1$, *where* σ_1 *and* σ_2 *are reflections. Let* l_1 *and* l_2 *be the axes of* σ_1 *and* σ_2, *and suppose that* τ *is the translation associated with the vector* **a**. *Then* l_1 *and* l_2 *are both perpendicular to* **a**. *Subject to this condition, we may choose either* σ_1 *or* σ_2 *arbitrarily, but our choice then fixes the other.*

Consider next the rotation $\rho = \sigma_2 \sigma_1$, *where* σ_1 *and* σ_2 *are reflections. Let* l_1 *and* l_2 *be the axes of* σ_1 *and* σ_2, *and let the center of the rotation be the point* O. *Then* l_1 *and* l_2 *both pass through* O. *Subject to this condition, we may choose either* σ_1 *or* σ_2 *arbitrarily, but our choice then fixes the other.*

We leave the proofs of these statements, which are quite easy, to the reader.

10. Orthogonal Transformations of the Plane in Coordinates

Let us introduce in the plane a rectangular Cartesian system of coordinates xOy with unit points E_1 and E_2. Let $M(x, y)$ be any point of the plane and $M'(x', y')$ its image under the orthogonal transformation α. In this section we shall derive formulas expressing the coordinates x', y' of M' in terms of the coordinates x, y of M (all in the given coordinate system).

10.1. TRANSLATION

Let τ be the plane translation determined by the vector **t**. Suppose that in the given coordinate system **t** has the coordinates a, b (Fig. 38). Let x, y, x', y' be as above, where $\alpha = \tau$.

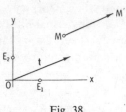

Fig. 38

Then, by definition, $\overrightarrow{MM'} = \mathbf{t}$. This means that the coordinates of $\overrightarrow{MM'}$ are a and b (since two vectors are equal if and only if they have the same coordinates). But the coordinates of $\overrightarrow{MM'}$ are the differences between the coordinates of its endpoint and its initial point: that is, $x' - x$, $y' - y$.

So we have $x' - x = a$; $y' - y = b$; and

$$x' = x + a; \qquad y' = y + b.$$

This is the expression for a translation, written coordinatewise. We may also write it $\tau(x, y) = (x + a, y + b)$.

10.2. REFLECTION IN A LINE

We shall consider only reflection in a line through O, for a reason that will appear in Section 10.5.

Let l be a line through O making an oriented angle γ with the x axis. Let M be an arbitrary point other than O, and let (r, θ) be its polar coordinates. That is, $OM = r$, and the oriented angle $xOM = \theta$. Then (Fig. 39), the

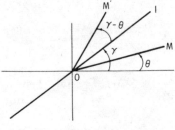

Fig. 39

polar coordinates of M' are $(r, 2\gamma - \theta)$. So

$$x' = r\cos(2\gamma - \theta) = r\cos 2\gamma \cos\theta + r\sin 2\gamma \sin\theta;$$
$$y' = r\sin(2\gamma - \theta) = r\sin 2\gamma \cos\theta - r\cos 2\gamma \sin\theta.$$

But

$$x = r\cos\theta,$$
$$y = r\sin\theta.$$

So

$$x' = x\cos 2\gamma + y\sin 2\gamma,$$
$$y' = x\sin 2\gamma - y\cos 2\gamma. \tag{1}$$

This is the equation of the reflection in the line *l*. Note that the addition formulas for sin and cos that we used, as well as the formulas $x = r \cos \theta$, $y = r \sin \theta$ for the point $M(x, y)$ with polar coordinates (r, θ), are true *only* when we take α and θ to be oriented angles.

We did not consider the formula for the point into which O is taken, but we see at once that (1) is valid for it too.

Note the special cases where l is the x axis or the y axis. In the first case, $\gamma = 0$, and (1) reduces to

$$x' = x, \qquad y' = -y.$$

In the second case, $\gamma = \pi/2$, and the formula reduces to

$$x' = -x, \qquad y' = y.$$

10.3. REFLECTION IN A POINT

We take the point to be the origin O (Fig. 40). Then, for any point $M(x, y)$, the point M' symmetrically opposite it with respect to the origin is $M(x', y')$, where

$$x' = -x, \qquad y' = -y. \tag{2}$$

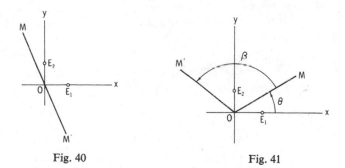

Fig. 40   Fig. 41

10.4. ROTATION

We take the center of the rotation to be the origin (Fig. 41). Let ρ be the rotation about O through the oriented angle β. Let M be any point of the plane other that O, and (r, θ) its polar coordinates. If $\rho(M) = M'$, then clearly the polar coordinates of M' are $(r, \theta + \beta)$. So if $M' = M'(x', y')$, we have

$$x' = r \cos(\theta + \beta) = r \cos \theta \cos \beta - r \sin \theta \sin \beta,$$

$$y' = r \sin(\theta + \beta) = r \cos \theta \sin \beta + r \sin \theta \cos \beta.$$

But $x = r \cos \theta$, $y = r \sin \theta$, so that

$$x' = x \cos \beta - y \sin \beta;$$
$$y' = x \sin \beta + y \cos \beta. \tag{3}$$

This formula for the result of a rotation clearly holds also for the point O. Note that the case of Section 10.3 (that of reflection in O) is obtained from (3) by taking $\beta = \pi$; that is, reflection in a point is the same as rotation through two right angles.

10.5. The General Case

I.   Suppose now that α is any orthogonal transformation of the first kind, and $\alpha(O) = O'(a, b)$. We introduce a new system of coordinates with origin at O' and axes parallel to the old. Let us use the notation $M(x, y) = M'(x^*, y^*)$ to mean that the point whose coordinates in the old system are x, y has coordinates x^*, y^* in the new system. Then $M(x, y) = M'(x - a, y - b)$. Let τ be the translation which takes O into O'. Then $\alpha = \alpha'\tau$, where α' is another orthogonal transformation of the first kind, which leaves O' fixed. By a result in Section 8, α' is the rotation about O' through an oriented angle of, say, β.

Then, for any point $M(x, y)$, we have

$$\alpha(M(x, y)) = \alpha'\tau(M(x, y)) = \alpha'(M(x + a, y + b))$$

$$= \alpha'(M'(x, y))$$

$$= M'(x \cos \beta - y \sin \beta, x \sin \beta + y \cos \beta)$$

$$= M(x \cos \beta - y \sin \beta + a, x \sin \beta + y \cos \beta + b).$$

Thus we have

$$x' = x \cos \beta - y \sin \beta + a;$$
$$y' = x \sin \beta + y \cos \beta + b. \tag{4}$$

Note that we have incidentally proved the following theorem:

Theorem I. *A given orthogonal transformation α of the first kind may be expressed in the form $\alpha = \rho\tau\ (\alpha = \tau'\rho')$, for some translation $\tau\ (\tau')$ and rotation $\rho\ (\rho')$, if and only if $\rho\ (\rho')$ is a rotation through a certain fixed angle β, determined by α.*

If the center of ρ is O', then τ is the translation along the vector $\overrightarrow{OO'}$, where O is the inverse image under α of O'; if the center of ρ' is O, then τ' is the translation through $\overrightarrow{OO'}$, where $O' = \alpha(O)$.

II.   Suppose that α is an orthogonal transformation of the second kind. Let $\alpha(O) = O'(a, b)$, and let τ be the translation through the vector $\overrightarrow{OO'}$. Then $\alpha = \alpha'\tau$, where α' is a transformation of the second kind leaving O' fixed. By a result in Section 8, α' is a reflection in a line through O'. We introduce new coordinates as before, and since in these coordinates α' is given by Eq. (1), we find, as before, that $\alpha(M(x, y)) = (x', y')$, where

$$x' = x \cos 2\gamma + y \sin 2\gamma + a,$$
$$y' = x \sin 2\gamma - y \cos 2\gamma + b. \tag{5}$$

We also have:

Theorem 2. *A given orthogonal transformation α of the second kind may be expressed in the form $\alpha = \sigma\tau(\alpha = \tau'\sigma')$, for some translation $\tau(\tau')$ and reflection $\sigma(\sigma')$, if and only if $\sigma(\sigma')$ is the reflection in some line $l(l')$ parallel to a given line m determined by α.*

Here m is any line making an oriented angle γ with the x axis, in our notation. If O' is any point on the axis l of σ, then τ is the translation through $\overrightarrow{OO'}$, where O is the inverse image of O'. Similarly, if O is any point on l', τ' is the translation through the vector $\overrightarrow{OO'}$, where O' is the image of O.

Note that the general equation [Eq. (4) or (5)] is linear in the coordinates and that, if α is of the first kind, its determinant is equal to $+1$:

$$\begin{vmatrix} \cos \beta & -\sin \beta \\ \sin \beta & \cos \beta \end{vmatrix} = +1;$$

whereas if it is of the second kind, its determinant is -1:

$$\begin{vmatrix} \cos 2\gamma & \sin 2\gamma \\ \sin 2\gamma & -\cos 2\gamma \end{vmatrix} = -1.$$

It may be suggested that the sign indicates whether the transformation preserves orientation, and its absolute value, 1, indicates that areas are multiplied by a factor of 1.

II. Orthogonal Transformations in Space

Orthogonal transformations in space are defined in exactly the same way as for the plane and, like those in the plane, fall into two classes—transformations of the first and second kind—according to whether they do or do not preserve orientation.

If A, B, C, D are four non-coplanar points and if A', B', C', D' are four points such that $AB = A'B'$, $AC = A'C'$, $AD = A'D'$, $BC = B'C'$, $BD = B'D'$, and $CD = C'D'$, then there is a unique orthogonal transformation taking A, B, C, D to A', B', C', D', respectively.

If A, B, C are any three noncollinear points and A', B', C' three points such that the triangles ABC and $A'B'C'$ are congruent, then there is a unique orthogonal transformation of each kind (first and second) taking A into A', etc. The proofs of these theorems may be carried out similarly to the planar case (Theorem 8, Section 5, and Theorem 2, Section 7).

The set of all orthogonal transformations of space is a group, and the subset of all transformations of the first kind is a subgroup of this group.

The fundamental types of orthogonal transformation in space are translation, reflection in a plane, rotation about a line (including rotation through two right angles, which is reflection in the line), and reflection in a point.

11.1. TRANSLATION

A translation is defined exactly as in the plane: each point M is taken into the point M' for which $\overrightarrow{MM'} = \mathbf{a}$, where $\mathbf{a}$ is a given fixed vector. Translation is an orthogonal transformation of the first kind. That it is an orthogonal transformation may be proved as in the case of the plane; we now show that it is of the first kind. Let A be any point, A' its image, and π any plane through AA'. Then α induces an orthogonal transformation on π. Let ABC be any triangle in π, and let $A'B'C'$ be its image under α. Then $A'B'C'$ lies in π and has the same orientation as ABC. Let S be any point not in π and S' its image under α. Consider any chain D of triangles joining ABC to $A'B'C'$; the number of pairs of adjacent triangles in D that have opposite orientations is even. Let D' be the chain of tetrahedra joining $ABCS$ to $A'B'C'S$, obtained from D by letting S be the fourth vertex of each tetrahedron, the other vertices being those of the triangles of D in order. The reader should verify that D' is a chain and that adjacent tetrahedra in the sequence have the same orientation if and only if the corresponding triangles in D have the same orientation. It follows that the number of pairs of adjacent tetrahedra that have opposite orientation is even, so that $ABCS$ and $A'B'C'S$ have the same orientation. But $A'B'C'S$ and $A'B'C'S'$ have the same orientation, since S and S' lie on the same side of π, and therefore so do $ABCS$ and $A'B'C'S'$. This shows that α is of the first kind.

In order that an orthogonal transformation be a translation, it is necessary and sufficient that every vector $\overrightarrow{AB}$ be transformed into an equal vector $\overrightarrow{A'B'}$. The proof is just as for the case of the plane. The set of all translations in space (including the identity transformation, which is the translation by the zero vector) forms a subgroup of the group of orthogonal transformations of the first kind.

11.2. REFLECTION IN A PLANE

Suppose we are given a plane π in space. We place in correspondence with each point M of space its reflection M' in π. That is to say, π is the perpendicular bisector of MM'. The points of π itself are placed in correspondence with themselves.

Such a transformation is called the *reflection in* π. As in the planar case, we may show that reflection in a plane is an orthogonal transformation of the second kind. It is also true that α is the reflection in a plane if and only if there are three non-collinear points which remain invariant under α, and α is not the identity. The proof is as in the planar case, the plane π of reflection being the plane through the given three points.

11.3. REFLECTION IN A LINE

Suppose we are given a line l in space. We place in correspondence with each point M of space its reflection M' in l. That is to say, the lines MM' and l intersect in the midpoint of the former and at right angles. The points of l are put in correspondence with themselves. Such a transformation is called a *reflection* (the reflection in the line l), and l is called its *axis*.

Reflection in a line is an orthogonal transformation of space of the first kind. For any segment parallel to the axis is transformed into an equal segment also parallel to it. Any segment lying in a plane π perpendicular to l is transformed into an equal and parallel segment lying in π (since α induces in π the transformation that reflects each point of π in the point O of intersection of π with l). Suppose now MN is a segment neither parallel nor perpendicular to l. Let π be the plane through M perpendicular to l, and let P be the base of the perpendicular from N to π. Let M', N', P' be the reflections in l of M, N, P, respectively. Then, by what we have already said, $M'P' = MP$, and $N'P' = NP$. Since MPN and $M'P'N'$ are both right-angled triangles, it follows that $M'N' = MN$.

We show now that reflection in l is a transformation of the first kind. Let O and S be any points of l and A and B be points of the plane π through O and perpendicular to l but not collinear with O. Let A', B' be the reflections in l of A and B, respectively. Then the triangles AOB and $A'OB'$ both lie in π and have the same orientation, since they are reflections of each other in O. It follows, by the same argument as in the section on translations, that the tetrahedra $SAOB$ and $SA'OB'$ also have the same orientation.

11.4. ROTATION

Let l be any line of space and β a fixed oriented angle. For an arbitrary point M not on l, let π be the plane through M and perpendicular to l, and suppose that π intersects l in O. Then we put in correspondence with M its image M' under the rotation of π with the center O and through the oriented angle β. We put each point of l in correspondence with itself. This

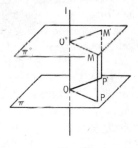

transformation of space is called the *rotation about l through β*, and it is an orthogonal transformation of the first kind. To prove this, we note first that, if MP is a segment parallel to l, then its image under α is an equal segment also parallel to l (see Fig. 42). For the triangles OPP' and O^*MM' are congruent (two equal sides and the included angle β), and since OO^* and PM are perpendicular to π, so too

Fig. 42

must $P'M'$ be. It is clear also that the image of a line segment PN perpendicular to l is an equal segment. The proof that the image of any line segment MN is an equal segment is now completed as in Section 11.3. The proof that the rotation is of the first kind is identical to the proof for the case of a reflection in l (11.3).

A rotation about a line is uniquely determined by its axis l and a pair of corresponding points A and A' not on l. For if π is the plane through A and A' perpendicular to l, and P is the point of intersection of l and π, then the rotation is through $\beta = \angle\, APA'$. Conversely, given a line l and points A and A' not on l, there exists a rotation with axis l taking A to A' if and only if A and A' are equidistant from l, and $AA' \perp l$.

The set of all rotations about a given line l forms a group (of course, we include the rotation through π, that is, the reflection in l; and the rotation through 0, that is, the identity transformation). In fact, each rotation is associated with an oriented angle in exactly the same way as the case of a plane rotation about a given point, and the group of space rotations about a line and plane rotations about a point are effectively the same. These groups are infinite and commutative.

11.5. Reflection in a Point

Let O be a fixed point of space. Let us make correspond to each point M of space its reflection M' in O. That is, O is the midpoint of the line segment MM'. We made O correspond to itself. The transformation we have thus defined is called the *reflection in O*, and O is called its *center*.

A reflection of space in a point is an orthogonal transformation of the second kind. For let M and N be any two points not collinear with O and π the plane through O, M, N. Then the reflection induces a reflection about O in the plane π, and since we already know this reflection is an orthogonal map, we conclude that $M'N' = MN$ (of course, M' and N' lie in π). If O lies on MN, we leave the proof to the reader.

To show that the transformation is of the second kind, let $OABC$ be any tetrahedron, and consider the chain of tetrahedra

$$OABC, \quad OABC', \quad OAB'C', \quad OA'B'C'.$$

The members of any successive pairing of these tetrahedra have opposite orientations, a total of three orientation changes. Thus $OA'B'C'$ has the opposite orientation from $OABC$.

12. Representation of an Orthogonal Transformation of Space as a Product of Fundamental Orthogonal Transformations

Theorem I. (Chasles). *Any orthogonal transformation of the first kind having at least one fixed point is a rotation about an axis l passing through this point (in particular, it may be the reflection in l or the identity transformation).*

Proof. Let α be an orthogonal transformation of the first kind, having the fixed point O. It may be that α is the identity transformation, and we exclude this case. Let A be a point whose image B under α does not coincide with it, and let C be the image of B. Then $C \neq B$, since $BC = AB$. If $C = A$, and O, A, B are not collinear, then α has the same effect on O, A, B as the reflection σ in the line OD, where D is the midpoint of the segment AB. (Note that $OA = OB$.) Since α and σ are both of the first kind and have the same effect on three noncollinear points, they coincide, and α is a reflection. If, on the other hand, $OA = OB$ lie on the same line for every choice of A, then α would clearly be the reflection in O—a contradiction, since this reflection is of the second kind.

Suppose finally that A, B, C are all distinct. A and B are not reflections of each other in O, since otherwise the line AOB would be mapped into BOC, so that the distinct lines AB and BC would have the two common points O and B. A, B, C cannot be collinear, since they are equidistant from O and are distinct in pairs. Let π and π' be the planes through O and perpendicular to AB and BC, respectively, and let l be their line of intersection. Then l is perpendicular to AB and to BC and, therefore, to the plane ABC. Let l meet this plane in O^*. Consider the tetrahedron OO^*AB. Its faces OO^*A and OO^*B are both right triangles, and since $OA = OB$ and OO^* is common, they are congruent. So $O^*A = O^*B$. Similarly $O^*B = O^*C$, and the triangles AO^*B and BO^*C are congruent (since they have three equal sides), and in particular $\gamma = \angle AO^* B = \angle BO^*C$. Let ρ be the rotation about l through the angle γ. Then clearly ρ takes A into B and B into C, and since (Section 11.4) it is of the first kind, we have $\alpha = \rho$. ▼

Theorem 2. *Any orthogonal transformation of the first kind either is the identity, a translation, or a rotation; or can be represented uniquely as the product $\gamma\beta$ of a rotation γ about some axis l and a translation β parallel to l. Moreover, $\gamma\beta = \beta\gamma$.*

Proof. Let α be an orthogonal transformation of the first kind.

If α is the identity, $\beta = \varepsilon = \gamma$. So suppose that it is not, and let A be a point such that $\alpha(A) = A' \neq A$. Let β be the translation which takes A into A'. Set $\gamma = \alpha\beta^{-1}$. Then γ is an orthogonal transformation of the first kind that leaves A' fixed, and so, by Theorem 1, it is the rotation about some axis l through A' (or the identity). If A lies on l, then $\alpha = \gamma\beta$ is the required representation of α. It is clear that $\gamma\beta = \beta\gamma$.

Suppose next that AA' does not lie on l. Set $\overrightarrow{AA'} = \overrightarrow{AP} + \overrightarrow{AQ}$, where $\overrightarrow{AP}$ is parallel to l and $\overrightarrow{AQ}$ is perpendicular to it (Fig. 43).

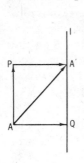

Fig. 43

Let β_1 and β_2 be the translations defined by the vectors $\overrightarrow{AP}$ and $\overrightarrow{AQ}$, respectively. Then $\beta = \beta_2\beta_1$, so that $\alpha = \gamma\beta_2\beta_1$. Set $\gamma\beta_2 = \gamma_1$. Then $\alpha = \gamma_1\beta_1$. We assert that this is the required representation of α. The transformation $\gamma_1 = \gamma\beta_2$ leaves every plane π perpendicular to l invariant as a whole. Thus it induces in each such plane an orthogonal transformation $\bar{\gamma}_1$, which is clearly of the first kind, since it is the product of a translation $\bar{\beta}_2$ through $\overrightarrow{PA'}$ and a rotation $\bar{\gamma}$ about the point A' of intersection of π with l (see Fig. 43). By Theorem 1 of Section 9, this is either a translation or a rotation. But if $\bar{\gamma}_1$ is a translation, then $\bar{\gamma} = \bar{\gamma}_1\bar{\beta}_2^{-1}$ is the product of two translations, and so is itself a translation, whereas we know that $\bar{\gamma}$ is a rotation. (We write a bar over a transformation to denote its restriction to the plane π.) Thus γ induces a rotation, indeed the same rotation, in every plane π perpendicular to l (where points of these planes are identified if one lies vertically above or below the other); the locus of the centers of all these rotations is a vertical line m, and γ_1 is a rotation about m.

Consider now the equation $\alpha = \gamma_1\beta_1$. If β_1 reduces to the identity (which happens when AA' is perpendicular to l), then $\alpha = \gamma_1$ is the rotation about m. If not, γ_1 is the rotation about a line parallel to l, and β_1 is a translation parallel to l, and so also parallel to m. In any case $\alpha = \gamma_1\beta_1$ is the required representation of α. It is clear that $\gamma_1\beta_1 = \beta_1\gamma_1$.

We must now prove the uniqueness of this representation. Under the transformation $\alpha = \gamma_1\beta_1$, the line m is carried into itself. We show that m is the only line with this property. We shall assume that neither γ_1 nor β_1 is the identity.

Let p be an arbitrary line, and suppose first it is skew to m. Let SP be the common perpendicular to m and p (S on m and P on p). Under α, m and p are transformed into skew lines m' and p', and SP goes into $S'P'$, which is distinct from SP, since S is taken by β_1 into a point S' distinct from it, and S' remains invariant under γ_1. Inasmuch as angles are preserved under orthogonal maps, $S'P'$ is the common perpendicular to m and p', so that, as it is not SP, p and p' must be distinct.

Suppose now that p intersects m in S. Then, under β_1, S goes into S', while under γ_1, S' remains in place. So, under α, S goes into the distinct point S'. But S' is the point of intersection of m and p', so that p' cannot be the same line as p.

Suppose finally that p is parallel to m. Then under β_1 it is transformed into itself, and under γ_1 it goes into a line p' parallel to p and m, but distinct from p.

We have thus shown that m is the only line invariant under α. Suppose that $\alpha = \gamma_0\beta_0$ for some reflection γ_0 in a line m_0 and translation β_0. Then, by what we have proved, the line m_0 (which is evidently invariant under $\alpha = \gamma_0\beta_0$) must be the line m. So γ_0 is a rotation about m, and β_0 is a translation along m. Now $\alpha = \gamma_1\beta_1 = \gamma_0\beta_0$, and $\gamma_0^{-1}\gamma_1 = \beta_0\beta_1^{-1}$. Since γ_0 and γ_1 are both rotations about m, so too are γ_0^{-1} and $\gamma_0^{-1}\gamma_1$, and since β_0 and β_1 are both translations parallel to m, β_1^{-1} and

$\beta_0\beta_1^{-1}$ are so also. Thus we find that a rotation about m is equal to a translation parallel to m. Under the rotation, every point of m remains fixed, so that the translation is the identity. But then the rotation is also the identity; that is, $\gamma_0^{-1}\gamma_1 = \beta_0\beta_1^{-1} = \varepsilon$. Hence $\gamma_0 = \gamma_1$ and $\beta_0 = \beta_1$.

We have now shown that if α has one representation $\alpha = \beta\gamma$ of the required type, and if neither of β and γ is the identity, then this representation is unique. There remains only the following case: in *every* representation of α of the required type, either β or γ is the identity. But then the other must be α, so that the representation is $\alpha = \alpha\varepsilon = \varepsilon\alpha$. In this case either α is a rotation, and ε is thought of as the identity translation, or α is a translation and ε is thought of as the identity rotation. ▼

Theorem 3. *Any orthogonal transformation α of the second kind either is a reflection in a plane or can be represented as the product of a reflection in a plane and a rotation about a line perpendicular to this plane or can be represented as the product of a reflection in a plane and a translation in some direction parallel to this plane, according as α has more than one fixed point, just one fixed point, or no fixed point.*

Such a representation is unique except in the second case when the rotation in the line is through two right angles. In this (and only in this) case, α is the reflection in a point O (the point of intersection of the line and the plane), and then it may be represented as the product of the reflection in any plane π through O and the rotation through two right angles about the line through O perpendicular to π.

Proof. Case 1. Let us suppose first that the orthogonal transformation α of the second kind has a fixed point O. Since α is not the identity (which is of the first kind), we may choose a point A whose image B under α does not coincide with it. Let C be the image of B. Then clearly C does not coincide with B.

If, for any point A, its image B lies on the line OA, then $OA = OB$, and therefore α is the reflection in the point O. The reflection can certainly be represented in the manner described in the second paragraph of the theorem. Moreover, it cannot be represented in any of the other ways there listed. For reflection in a plane followed by rotation in a perpendicular line is the only type of representation which leaves invariant a single point: the point of intersection of the line and the plane. Furthermore, reflection in the plane π, followed by rotation through an angle β about the perpendicular line l, is a reflection in the point O of intersection of π and l only if $\beta =$ two right angles.

Suppose next that B does not lie on OA, and suppose that C coincides with A. Then α is the reflection in the plane π through O and perpendicular to AB, since, like this reflection, it takes O, A, B into O, B, C, respectively, and both transformations are of the second kind.

Suppose next that B does not lie on OA, that C does not coincide with A, and that the four points O, A, B, C are co-planar. Then the transformation is the product of the reflection in this plane π and the rotation about the perpendicular l to π through O that takes A into B. For the reflection leaves O, A, B, C invariant, and the rotation leaves O invariant and takes A into B (such a rotation exists, since $OA = OB$), and also takes B into C, since the triangles AOB and BOC are congruent (three equal sides) and have the same orientation.

Suppose finally that B does not lie on OA, that C does not coincide with A, and that the four points $OABC$ are not co-planar. Let D be the midpoint of AB, E the midpoint of BC, and π the plane through ODE. Let l be the perpendicular through O to π. We show that α is the product of the reflection σ in π and a rotation ρ about l. For suppose that σ takes B into B^*. Then A, B^*, and C will all be on the same side of π and at equal distances from it. Let A_0, $B_0{}^*$, and C_0 be the projections of A, B^* and C onto π. Then, since $OA = OB^* = OC$, we have $OA_0 = OB_0{}^* = OC_0$. Next, AB^*B and CB^*B are both right triangles, since, for example, A and B^* are the same distance from π, so that AB^* is parallel to π, while BB^* is perpendicular to it. Also $AB = BC$. Thus the triangles AB^*B and CB^*B are congruent (since they are right triangles with a common side and equal hypotenuses). $AB^* = B^*C$, and therefore also $A_0B_0{}^* =$

B^*C_0 (since, for example, $AB^*B_0^*A_0$ is a rectangle). Finally, the triangles $OA_0B_0^*$ and $OB_0^*C_0$ are congruent (since they have three equal sides), and it follows that $\angle A_0OB_0^* = \angle B_0^*OC_0$.

Let ρ be the rotation about l that takes A_0 into B_0^* (this rotation exists, since π is perpendicular to l and $OA_0 = OB_0^*$). Then, by what we have just shown, ρ will take B_0^* into C_0. Since A, B^*, C are vertically "above" A_0, B_0^*, and C_0 and in a parallel plane, ρ will take A into B^* into C. Thus $\sigma\rho$ will, like α, take O, A, B into O, B, C, respectively, so that, since both these transformations are of the second kind, $\alpha = \sigma\rho$. It is clear also that $\sigma\rho = \rho\sigma$.

Case 2. Suppose now that α is an orthogonal transformation of the second kind, and that it has no fixed point. We shall need the following two lemmas:

Lemma I. *Let σ be the reflection in a plane π and β_2 a translation perpendicular to π. Then $\sigma\beta_2$ is the reflection in a plane π' parallel to π.*

Proof. Let A, B, C be any three noncollinear points of π, and A', B', C' their images under $\sigma\beta_2$. Then AA', BB', CC' are equal segments, all perpendicular to π. Let π' be the plane that passes through the midpoints of these segments. Then it is clear that π' is parallel to π and that the reflection σ_1 in the plane π' also takes A, B, C into A', B', C', respectively. Since $\sigma\beta_2$ and σ_1 are both of the second kind, they are equal.

Lemma 2. *Let ρ be a rotation (other than the identity) about a line l and β_1 a translation parallel to a plane π perpendicular to l. Then $\rho\beta_1$ is a rotation about a line n parallel to l.*

Proof. Let l meet π in O, and let P be the point (of π) such that β_1 is the translation associated with $\overrightarrow{PO}$. Let m be that perpendicular bisector of OP which lies in the plane π. Suppose that ρ is the rotation about l through an oriented angle δ. Choose the point R on m for which the oriented angle $\angle PRO = \delta$. Then $\rho\beta_1$ is the rotation through δ about the line n through R and perpendicular to π (and so parallel to l). To prove this, we can consider the restrictions of all the maps to the plane π. The restriction of $\rho\beta_1$ is an orthogonal map of the first kind. Now β_1 takes R into the point Q for which $POQR$ is a parallelogram, and ρ takes Q through the oriented angle $\delta = \angle PRO = \angle QOR$ to the point R (since $QO = RP = RO$). Thus the restriction map is of the first kind and leaves R invariant, so it is the rotation about R. The same argument applies in every plane parallel to π, and the result follows immediately.

Let us return now to α and suppose that $\alpha(A) = A'\ (\neq A)$. Let β be the translation through the vector $\overrightarrow{AA'}$. Then β takes A into A', and $\gamma = \alpha\beta^{-1}$ leaves A' invariant. But it is clear that γ is an orthogonal map of the second kind. So, by the first part of this proof, $\gamma = \sigma\rho$ is the product of the reflection σ in a plane π through A' and a rotation ρ about the perpendicular l to π through A'. (A representation of this form need not be unique, and ρ may be the identity.) Let us represent β in the form $\beta = \beta_1\beta_2$, where β_1 is a translation parallel to π, and β_2 is a translation perpendicular to π (and so parallel to l). Such a representation for β is always possible (in fact, is uniquely possible). Then $\alpha = \sigma\rho\beta_1\beta_2$.

Suppose now that ρ is not the identity. Then, by Lemma 2, $\rho\beta_1$ is a rotation ρ_1 about a line n perpendicular to π. So

$$\alpha = \sigma\rho\beta_1\beta_2 = \sigma\rho_1\beta_2 = \rho_1\sigma\beta_2 .$$

Next, by Lemma 1, $\sigma\beta_2$ is a reflection σ_1 in a plane π' parallel to π, and $\alpha = \rho_1\sigma_1$. But then the point S of intersection of π' and n is invariant under α, which is contrary to hypothesis.

So ρ is the identity, and $\alpha = \sigma\beta_1\beta_2 = \sigma\beta_2\beta_1 = \sigma_1\beta_1$. This is the required representation of α.

Note that in each case in this theorem where α is represented as the product of two simple transformations, these transformations commute. Thus, in Case 1 we have $\alpha = \sigma\rho = \rho\sigma$, and, in Case 2, $\alpha = \sigma_1\beta_1 = \beta_1\sigma_1$.

We now have to prove the "uniqueness" part of the theorem. That is to say, we must prove that if α is an orthogonal transformation of the second kind, then its representation as the product of a reflection in a plane and a rotation about it (if it has fixed points), or of a reflection in a plane and a translation parallel to it (if not), is unique except for the case in which α is the reflection in a point.

Suppose first that $\alpha = \sigma\rho$, where σ is the reflection in a plane π and ρ is a rotation—not through two right angles and not the identity—about a line l perpendicular to π. Then π is the only plane invariant (as a whole) under α. For if λ is a parallel plane, its image is a plane λ' parallel to λ but on the other side of it from π, whereas if λ intersects π in the line m, then the image of m is a line m' distinct from m (this is where we use the fact that ρ is not a rotation through two right angles, for otherwise $m' = m$ if m passes through the point O of intersection of l with π). So λ', which intersects $\pi' = \pi$ in m', cannot be the same plane as λ.

Suppose now that α can also be represented in the form $\alpha = \sigma^*\rho^*$, where σ^* is the reflection in a plane π^*, and ρ^* is a rotation about a line perpendicular to π^*. Then π^* is invariant under $\sigma^*\rho^* = \alpha$, and so is equal to π. But then $\sigma^* = \sigma$, and so also $\rho^* = \rho$.

Suppose now that $\alpha = \beta\sigma$, where σ is the reflection in a plane π and β is a translation parallel to π. We allow the possibility that β is the identity. Then π is the only plane invariant under α whose orientation is preserved. For suppose first that the plane λ is parallel to π. Then its image under α is a plane λ' parallel to λ but on the other side of π from it. Suppose next that λ intersects π in the line m. Then if λ is invariant under α (which happens provided that λ is perpendicular to π and, if β is not the identity, m is parallel to the vector associated with β), α induces in λ the reflection in m, which is an orthogonal transformation of the second kind. In π, α induces the translation β, so that our assertion is proved.

Suppose that α has another representation $\alpha = \beta^*\sigma^*$, where σ^* is the reflection in a plane π^* and β^* is a translation parallel to it. Then, by what we have just proved, π^* is the only plane invariant under α whose orientation is preserved. But this means that $\pi^* = \pi$ and hence also that $\sigma^* = \sigma$ and $\beta^* = \beta$. ▼

Theorem 4. *Any orthogonal transformation of the first kind can be represented as the product of two or four reflections in planes, and any orthogonal transformation of the first kind either is itself a reflection in a plane or can be represented as the product of three such.*

Proof. Let α be an orthogonal transformation of the first kind. Then, by Theorem 1, it either is a rotation or a translation or can be represented as the product of a rotation and a translation.

(1) Suppose first that α is a rotation about a line l. Let π_1 be any plane through l, and let π_2 be its image under α. Let π be the bisector of these planes lying inside the oriented angle π_1/π_2. Let σ be the reflection in π and σ_2 the reflection in π_2. Then $\sigma_2\sigma$ takes π_1 into π_2, and since it, like α, is of the first kind, $\alpha = \sigma_2\sigma$.

(2) Suppose next that α is the translation determined by the vector $\overrightarrow{AA'}$. Let π be the plane that bisects AA' at right angles and π' the plane through A' parallel to π. Let σ and σ' be the reflections in these two planes. It is clear that $\alpha = \sigma'\sigma$.

(3) Suppose finally that α can be represented as the product $\rho\tau$ of a rotation and a translation. On substituting the product of two reflections for each of ρ and τ (by parts 1 and 2 of this proof), we find that α can be represented as the product of four reflections.

Suppose now that α is of the second kind. Then, by Theorem 3, either it is the reflection in some plane (in which case we are through) or it can be represented as the product of a reflection and a rotation or a translation. But either a translation or a rotation can be represented as the product of two reflections, so α can be represented as the product of three. ▼

Note I. Since the product of two transformations of the same kind is of the first kind, while the product of two transformations of different kinds is of the second kind (we may think of transformations of the first kind as positive and those of the second kind as negative), and since reflection in a plane is of the second kind, any representation of a transformation of the first kind by reflections must have an even number of reflections, while any representation of a transformation of the second kind by reflections must have an odd number. Theorem 4 is "best possible" in the sense that, although any transformation that can be represented as a product of n reflections can also be represented as a product of $(n + 2m)$ reflections for any positive integer m, we cannot reduce the number of reflections required below that which is stated in Theorem 4. This is clear for transformations of the second kind and for rotations and translations (a product of 0 reflections may be taken to mean the identity transformation), but if α is of the first kind and not a rotation or a translation, it cannot be represented as a product of two reflections (the only possible number less than 4). For if these reflections are in planes π and π', and π and π' are parallel, then α is a translation in the direction of their common perpendicular, whereas if π and π' intersect in the line l, then α is a rotation about l.

Note 2. The representation of a transformation as a product of reflections is not unique. If α is a rotation or a translation, the situation is analogous to that of Theorem 4, Section 9, but in general it is more complicated.

13. Orthogonal Transformations of Space in Coordinates

Let us introduce in space a system of rectangular Cartesian coordinates with origin O and unit points E_1, E_2, E_3.

Let us place in correspondence with each point $M(x, y, z)$ of space the point $M'(x', y', z')$ whose coordinates are given by the linear equations

$$x' = a_{11}x + a_{12}y + a_{13}z + a,$$
$$y' = a_{21}x + a_{22}y + a_{23}z + b,$$
$$z' = a_{31}x + a_{32}y + a_{33}z + c,$$

where

$$\left.\begin{aligned}
a_{11}^2 + a_{21}^2 + a_{31}^2 &= 1, \\
a_{12}^2 + a_{22}^2 + a_{32}^2 &= 1, \\
a_{13}^2 + a_{23}^2 + a_{33}^2 &= 1, \\
a_{11}a_{12} + a_{21}a_{22} + a_{31}a_{32} &= 0, \\
a_{12}a_{13} + a_{22}a_{23} + a_{32}a_{33} &= 0, \\
a_{13}a_{11} + a_{23}a_{21} + a_{33}a_{31} &= 0.
\end{aligned}\right\} \tag{2}$$

We shall show that this mapping of space into itself is an orthogonal transformation. To do so, we need to show that, for any two points $M_1(x_1, y_1, z_1)$ and $M_2(x_2, y_2, z_2)$, the distance $M_1'M_2'$ between their images $M_1'(x_1', y_1', z_1')$ and $M_2'(x_2', y_2', z_2')$ is the same as the distance M_1M_2 between them.

But

$$M_1'M_2'^2 = (x_2' - x_1')^2 + (y_2' - y_1')^2 + (z_2' - z_1')^2$$

$$= [(a_{11}x_2 + a_{12}y_2 + a_{13}z_2 + a)$$
$$- (a_{11}x_1 + a_{12}y_1 + a_{13}z_1 + a)]^2$$
$$+ [(a_{21}x_2 + a_{22}y_2 + a_{23}z_2 + b)$$
$$- (a_{21}x_1 + a_{22}y_1 + a_{23}z_1 + b)]^2$$
$$+ [(a_{31}x_2 + a_{32}y_2 + a_{33}z_2 + c)$$
$$- (a_{31}x_1 + a_{32}y_1 + a_{33}z_1 + c)]^2$$

$$= [a_{11}(x_2 - x_1) + a_{12}(y_2 - y_1) + a_{13}(z_2 - z_1)]^2$$
$$+ [a_{21}(x_2 - x_1) + a_{22}(y_2 - y_1) + a_{23}(z_2 - z_1)]^2$$
$$+ [a_{31}(x_2 - x_1) + a_{32}(y_2 - y_1) + a_{33}(z_2 - z_1)]^2$$

$$= (a_{11}^2 + a_{21}^2 + a_{31}^2)(x_2 - x_1)^2 + (a_{12}^2 + a_{22}^2 + a_{32}^2)(y_2 - y_1)^2$$

$$+ (a_{13}^2 + a_{23}^2 + a_{33}^2)(z_2 - z_1)^2$$

$$+ 2(a_{11}a_{12} + a_{21}a_{22} + a_{31}a_{32})(x_2 - x_1)(y_2 - y_1)$$

$$+ 2(a_{12}a_{13} + a_{22}a_{23} + a_{32}a_{33})(y_2 - y_1)(z_2 - z_1)$$

$$+ 2(a_{13}a_{11} + a_{23}a_{21} + a_{33}a_{31})(z_2 - z_1)(x_2 - x_1)$$

$$= (x_2 - x_1)^2 + (y_2 - y_1)^2 + (z_2 - z_1)^2 = M_1M_2{}^2,$$

by the relations (2).

We shall now show that if α is any orthogonal transformation taking the typical point $M(x, y, z)$ into $M'(x', y', z')$, then α is given by formulas of the form (1) and that, moreover, the relations (2) are satisfied. Suppose that $O'(a, b, c)$, $E_1'(p_1, q_1, r_1)$, $E_2'(p_2, q_2, r_2)$, $E_3'(p_3, q_3, r_3)$ are the images of $O(0, 0, 0)$, $E_1(1, 0, 0)$, $E_2(0, 1, 0)$, $E_3(0, 0, 1)$, respectively.

Let us define the numbers a_{ij} by

$$a_{11} = p_1 - a, \qquad a_{12} = p_2 - a, \qquad a_{13} = p_3 - a,$$

$$a_{21} = q_1 - b, \qquad a_{22} = q_2 - b, \qquad a_{23} = q_3 - b, \qquad (3)$$

$$a_{31} = r_1 - c, \qquad a_{32} = r_2 - c, \qquad a_{33} = r_3 - c.$$

Then

$$a_{11}^2 + a_{21}^2 + a_{31}^2 = (p_1 - a)^2 + (q_1 - b)^2 + (r_1 - c)^2$$

$$= O'E_1'^2 = OE_1{}^2 = 1,$$

and, similarly,

$$a_{12}^2 + a_{22}^2 + a_{23}^2 = 1,$$

$$a_{13}^2 + a_{23}^2 + a_{33}^2 = 1.$$

Next, since α is orthogonal, $E_1'O'E_2'$ is a right triangle and also $O'E_1' = O'E_2' = 1$. So,

$$E_1'E_2'^2 = O'E_1'^2 + O'E_2'^2 = 2$$

or

$$(p_2 - p_1)^2 + (q_2 - q_1)^2 + (r_2 - r_1)^2 = 2$$

or

$$(a_{11} - a_{12})^2 + (a_{21} - a_{22})^2 + (a_{31} - a_{32})^2 = 2,$$

$$a_{11}^2 + a_{21}^2 + a_{31}^2 - 2(a_{11}a_{12} + a_{21}a_{22} + a_{31}a_{32})$$

$$+ a_{12}^2 + a_{22}^2 + a_{32}^2 = 2.$$

But

$$a_{11}^2 + a_{21}^2 + a_{31}^2 = a_{12}^2 + a_{22}^2 + a_{32}^2 = 1,$$

so that

$$a_{11}a_{12} + a_{21}a_{22} + a_{31}a_{32} = 0.$$

The last two equations in (2) are proved similarly.

Let the orthogonal transformation β be defined by the formulas (1), where the a_{ij} are given by (3). Then it is clear that β has the same effect as α on the four non-coplanar points O, E_1, E_2, E_3. By a result stated at the beginning of Section 11, $\beta = \alpha$. We have thus proved that a transformation α of space is orthogonal if and only if its expression in terms of coordinates is given by (1) and the relations (2) are satisfied.

The reader may feel that the treatment we have given in this section is somewhat artificial; we seem to have pulled Eqs. (1) and the relations (2) out of a hat, and then proved that any orthogonal transformation can be expressed in this form, so to speak, backwards. The reader with a little knowledge of vector algebra may find the treatment that follows more natural.

Suppose we are given a system of rectangular Cartesian coordinates in space, with origin O. We identify each point $M(x_1, x_2, x_3)$ of space with the vector $\overrightarrow{OM} = \mathbf{x}$, so that $\mathbf{x}$ is the vector whose coordinates are (x_1, x_2, x_3). We shall say that a mapping α of space is *linear* provided the following conditions are satisfied:

$$\alpha(a\mathbf{x}) = a(\alpha(\mathbf{x})), \tag{4}$$

$$\alpha(\mathbf{x} + \mathbf{y}) = \alpha(\mathbf{x}) + \alpha(\mathbf{y}), \tag{5}$$

for all vectors **x** and **y** and all numbers a. In particular, a linear mapping takes the origin into itself.

Suppose now that α is an orthogonal transformation leaving O invariant. We show that it is a linear mapping. We shall typically write **x**′ for the image under α of the vector **x**.

Let **x** be any vector and a any real number. Then O, $M(\mathbf{x})$, $N(a\mathbf{x})$ are collinear, so that their images O, $M'(\mathbf{x}')$, $N'((a\mathbf{x})')$ are also collinear. Suppose first that a is positive. Then $ON = aOM$, and M and N lie on the same side of O. But then $\overrightarrow{ON'} = aOM'$, and N' and M' lie on the same side of O. Since N' lies on OM', we have $(a\mathbf{x})' = a\mathbf{x}'$. If a is negative, $ON' = |a|OM'$, and since in this case M' and N' lie on the same line through O but on opposite sides of it, $\overrightarrow{ON'} = -|a|\overrightarrow{OM'} = a\overrightarrow{OM'}$; that is, $(a\mathbf{x})' = a\mathbf{x}'$. We have thus proved (4), the case where $a = 0$ being trivial.

Suppose next that $M(\mathbf{x})$ and $N(\mathbf{y})$ are any vectors (points). Then the midpoint P of MN is $P(\frac{1}{2}(\mathbf{x} + \mathbf{y}))$. Under α, P goes into the midpoint P' of $M'N'$; that is, $P'(\frac{1}{2}(\mathbf{x}' + \mathbf{y}'))$. So

$$\tfrac{1}{2}(\mathbf{x}' + \mathbf{y}') = (\tfrac{1}{2}(\mathbf{x} + \mathbf{y}))'.$$

Using (4) with $a = \frac{1}{2}$, we find that (5) follows from this. We have thus shown that an orthogonal transformation leaving the origin fixed is a linear mapping.

Suppose now that the orthogonal transformation α with fixed point O takes the unit vectors $\mathbf{e}_1$, $\mathbf{e}_2$, $\mathbf{e}_3$ into the vectors $\mathbf{a}_1$, $\mathbf{a}_2$, $\mathbf{a}_3$, where $\mathbf{a}_1$, for example, is the vector (a_{11}, a_{21}, a_{31}). Let $M(x, y, z)$ be a general point of space. Then $M = M(x\mathbf{e}_1 + y\mathbf{e}_2 + z\mathbf{e}_3)$. Since α is a linear transformation, $\alpha(M) = \alpha(x\mathbf{e}_1 + y\mathbf{e}_2 + z\mathbf{e}_3) = x\mathbf{a}_1 + y\mathbf{a}_2 + z\mathbf{a}_3$ [where we have used (4) and (5)]. On rewriting this in coordinates, we have (1), with $a = b = c = 0$.

Next, the length of $\mathbf{a}_i$ is $\mathbf{a}_i^2 = 1$, since $\mathbf{a}_i$ is the image of the unit vector $\mathbf{e}_i$ ($i = 1, 2, 3$). This gives us the first three relations of (2). Since $\mathbf{e}_i$ and $\mathbf{e}_j$ are perpendicular ($i = j$), so are $\mathbf{a}_i$ and $\mathbf{a}_j$. That is to say, $\mathbf{a}_i \cdot \mathbf{a}_j = 0$. This gives us the last three relations of (2). We have thus shown that an orthogonal transformation leaving the origin fixed is given by (1) (with $a = b = c = 0$) subject to the conditions (2). If α is an arbitrary orthogonal transformation, and $\alpha(O) = O'$, we set $\alpha = \beta\gamma$, where β is the translation through the vector $\overrightarrow{OO'} = (a, b, c)$. Then γ is an orthogonal transformation leaving O fixed, and so it is of the form we have just described. The translation β then takes $M(x, y, z)$ into $\gamma M(x, y, z) + \overrightarrow{OO'}$, which, written coordinate-wise, is just (1). We have thus proved that any orthogonal transformation can be expressed in the form (1), subject to (2).

Suppose next that α is the mapping of space given by (1) and that (2) is satisfied. We show that α is an orthogonal transformation. Let β be the translation through the vector (a, b, c); then $\alpha = \gamma\beta^{-1}$, where γ is the transformation given by (1) subject to (2), except that a, b, c have been deleted. It may be checked immediately that this map is linear, that is, satisfies (4) and (5) above. Also the images under γ of the $\mathbf{e}_i$ are the $\mathbf{a}_i$ defined as before ($i = 1, 2, 3$). The relations (2) then state that the $\mathbf{a}_i$ are mutually perpendicular unit vectors. We show now that this implies that γ is an orthogonal map. Let $P(\mathbf{p})$ and $Q(\mathbf{q})$ be any two points (vectors) and $P'(\mathbf{p}')$, $Q'(\mathbf{q}')$ their images under γ. If $\mathbf{p} = p_1\mathbf{e}_1 + p_2\mathbf{e}_2 + p_3\mathbf{e}_3$, then $\mathbf{p}' = p_1\mathbf{a}_1 + p_2\mathbf{a}_2 + p_3\mathbf{a}_3$, since γ is a linear map. Because of the relations $\mathbf{a}_i^2 = 1$ and $\mathbf{a}_i \cdot \mathbf{a}_j = 0$ ($i = j$), we have $\mathbf{p}' \cdot \mathbf{q}' = p_1q_1 + p_2q_2 + p_3q_3 = \mathbf{p} \cdot \mathbf{q}$ (since the $\mathbf{e}_i$ satisfy the same relations). In particular, taking $\mathbf{q} = \mathbf{p}$, we find $\mathbf{p}'^2 = \mathbf{p}^2$, and similarly $\mathbf{q}'^2 = \mathbf{q}^2$. Now

$$PQ^2 = (\mathbf{p} - \mathbf{q})^2 = \mathbf{p}^2 - 2\mathbf{p} \cdot \mathbf{q} + \mathbf{q}^2 = \mathbf{p}'^2 - 2\mathbf{p}' \cdot \mathbf{q}' + \mathbf{q}'^2$$

$$= (\mathbf{p}' - \mathbf{q}')^2 = P'Q'^2.$$

Thus γ preserves all lengths; that is, it is an orthogonal transformation. And since the translation β is also an orthogonal transformation, so is $\alpha = \beta\gamma$. We have finally shown that the transformation α is orthogonal if and only if it can be represented in the form (1), subject to (2).

Note 1. Since the $\mathbf{a}_i$ are unit vectors, a_{11}, a_{21}, a_{31} are the direction cosines of $O'E_1'$ in the given system of coordinates, that is, the cosines of the angles that $O'E_1'$ makes with the respective axes—and similarly for the coordinates of $\mathbf{a}_2$ and $\mathbf{a}_3$. Since the $\mathbf{a}_i$ are mutually orthogonal, we could take them as a new system of rectangular coordinates, and the direction cosines in this system of Ox, Oy, Oz are clearly (a_{11}, a_{12}, a_{13}), and so on. Let us forget for the moment about the translation part of α, taking $a = b = c = 0$. Then $\alpha = \gamma$ takes E_i into E_i' and leaves O fixed. It follows that the inverse transformation γ^{-1} takes E_i' into E_i and leaves O fixed. But, in the new system of coordinates, the equation for γ^{-1} is just (1) with the rows and columns of the array (a_{ij}) interchanged (by the remark we just made about direction cosines). Since γ^{-1} is certainly an orthogonal transformation, we conclude that

$$a_{i1}^2 + a_{i2}^2 + a_{i3}^2 = 1 \qquad (i = 1, 2, 3),$$

and

$$a_{i1}a_{j1} + a_{i2}a_{j2} + a_{i3}a_{j3} = 0 \qquad (ij = 12, 23, 31).$$

It is a remarkable algebraic fact that the relations (2) imply in this way these "reciprocal" relations, and the reader is invited to deduce them directly. The theory of orthogonal transformations of space treated coordinatewise can be further developed by the use of matrix theory: the interested reader is referred to Leonid Mirsky, "An Introduction to Linear Algebra," Oxford Univ. (Clarendon) Press, 1955, or any book on linear algebra.

Note 2. If α is an orthogonal transformation of the first kind, the tetrahedra $OE_1E_2E_3$ and $OE_1'E_2'E_3'$ have the same orientation, and, in this case,

$$\Delta = \begin{vmatrix} a_{11} & a_{12} & a_{13} \\ a_{21} & a_{22} & a_{23} \\ a_{31} & a_{32} & a_{33} \end{vmatrix} = 1, \qquad (6)$$

while if α is an orthogonal transformation of the second kind, $\Delta = -1$. In fact, Δ is related to the expression for the (oriented!) volume of the oriented tetrahedron $OE_1'E_2'E_3'$. In general, the volume of the oriented tetrahedron $ABCD$ is the absolute value of the determinant

$$E = \begin{vmatrix} a_1 & a_2 & a_3 & 1 \\ b_1 & b_2 & b_3 & 1 \\ c_1 & c_2 & c_3 & 1 \\ d_1 & d_2 & d_3 & 1 \end{vmatrix} \tag{7}$$

(with the obvious notation), and in the case where one of the vertices is O, this expression reduces to (6) above. The sign of E is positive or negative according to whether $ABCD$ has the same orientation as $OE_1E_2E_3$ or the opposite orientation.

Note 3. The formulas and theorems we have proved for orthogonal transformations in three-dimensional space have very obvious extensions to spaces of higher dimension; we can define points or vectors with n coordinates instead of three, define distance by the obvious extension of Pythagoras' rule, and define orthogonal transformations. Then, for example, the generalizations of (1) and (2) will hold, and we can define orientation and "volume" of "simplexes" (generalized tetrahedra) by the analogs of (7) above. It will also turn out that the orthogonal transformation given by the array (a_{ij}) (with i and j running from 1 to n) will be of the first or second kind according to whether the determinant analogous to Δ above is equal to $+1$ or -1. The reader should check that Eqs. (4) and (5) in Section 10.5 satisfy the two-dimensional analog of Eqs. (1) and (2) in this section and that the corresponding statement about the analog of Δ is true.

Below we give the array (a_{ij}) associated [as in Eq. (1)] with the following orthogonal transformations, respectively: rotation through β about Oz, reflection in the plane $x \sin \alpha -$

$y \cos \alpha = 0$, reflection in the plane xOy, and reflection in O.

$$(1) \quad \begin{pmatrix} \cos \beta & -\sin \beta & 0 \\ \sin \beta & \cos \beta & 0 \\ 0 & 0 & 1 \end{pmatrix}, \quad (2) \quad \begin{pmatrix} \cos 2\alpha & \sin 2\alpha & 0 \\ \sin 2\alpha & -\cos 2\alpha & 0 \\ 0 & 0 & 1 \end{pmatrix},$$

$$(3) \quad \begin{pmatrix} 1 & 0 & 0 \\ 0 & 1 & 0 \\ 0 & 0 & -1 \end{pmatrix}, \quad (4) \quad \begin{pmatrix} -1 & 0 & 0 \\ 0 & -1 & 0 \\ 0 & 0 & -1 \end{pmatrix}.$$

Note added in proof. We conclude this chapter by calling attention to a very elegant result on length-preserving mappings, due to Peter Zvergnowski, of the University of Chicago. For details, see Appendix (p. 152).

CHAPTER III

Similarity Transformations

As we saw in the previous chapter, orthogonal transformations leave invariant both the shape and the dimensions of geometric figures. If we discard the demand that our transformations preserve dimension but still insist that shapes be preserved, the set of transformations we get is the group of similarity transformations (of the plane or of space). We shall see that such transformations increase or decrease all lengths in the same ratio but leave shapes unchanged.

Elementary geometry studies those properties of figures that are preserved under orthogonal transformations and also those properties that are preserved under similarity transformations. For example, such properties of a triangle as its area and the lengths of its sides are invariant under orthogonal transformations, but, in general, are not invariant under similarity transformations. On the other hand such properties as its angles or the position of its center of gravity are invariant under similarity transformations as well as under orthogonal transformations.

14. Similarity Mappings

A mapping α of a plane π into a plane π' is called a *similarity mapping* with coefficient $k > 0$, or simply a *similarity*, provided it has the following property: if A and B are any two points of

π, and A', B' are their images under α, then $A'B' = kAB$. If $k = 1$, α is an orthogonal mapping; and, conversely, any orthogonal mapping of π onto π' is a similarity with coefficient $k = 1$. We shall show first that any mapping of π into π' that preserves all shapes must be a similarity.

Let α be a mapping of the plane π into the plane π' such that the shape of the image triangle $A'B'C'$ is the same as the shape of any given triangle ABC in π. This is a weaker requirement than that α preserve *all* shapes, but we shall see that it is equivalent and also equivalent to the requirement that α be a similarity. Consider first the case where α maps every point of π onto a single point O of π'. Since the image of any figure in π is a single point, its shape is undefined, and we may, if we like, say that α preserves shapes by definition. But then we can also say that α is a (degenerate) similarity with coefficient $k = 0$. Conversely, any mapping α of π into π', which is a similarity except that the coefficient $k = 0$, maps every point of π onto a single point of π'. The proof is left to the reader. In the future, we exclude such degenerate mappings.

Suppose, then, that A, B are two points of π whose images A', B' under α are distinct. Let C, D be any two points of π, not both on AB. Then at least one of A and B does not lie on the line CD, say, for instance, A. Since not both of C and D lie on AB, suppose, for example, that C does not. Then ABC is a triangle similar to its image $A'B'C'$ in π'. We define the (positive) number k by the equation $A'B' = kAB$. Since the sides of similar triangles are in proportion, $A'C' = kAC$. Next, since A does not lie on CD, the triangle ACD is similar to its image $A'C'D'$, and since $A'C' = kAC$, we also have $C'D' = kCD$. We have thus shown that all segments not on AB have their lengths changed by a factor k under the mapping α. Now choose two points C, D not lying on AB and repeat the whole argument with C, D in place of A, B. We find that all lengths of segments not lying on CD, and, in particular, of all segments lying on AB, are changed by a factor k. We have thus shown that α is a similarity, and, since the image plane π' is a scale model of π (the scale factor being k), that α preserves *all* shapes.

It is clear that a similarity is one-one, and we may prove it is onto almost exactly as we proved the same for orthogonal maps (Section 4). So a similarity α has an inverse α^{-1}, and it is clear that α^{-1} is itself a similarity of π' onto π, with coefficient $1/k$.

A similarity α of π onto itself is called a *similarity trans- formation*. The product of two similarity transformations with coefficients k_1 and k_2 is a similarity transformation with coeffi- cient $k_1 k_2$. We regard the identity transformation as a simi- larity transformation with coefficient 1. It is clear then that the set of all similarity transformations (of a plane or of space) is a group, of which the orthogonal group is a subgroup.

I5. Properties of Similarity Transformations

Under a similarity transformation, the images of three collinear points A, B, C are three collinear points A', B', C'. For, if this is not so, then $A'B'C'$ is a triangle, and its image under the inverse transformation must be a similar triangle— a contradiction, since A, B, C are collinear. It is clear that if B lies between A and C, then B' lies between A' and C'. As in the previous chapter, we may show that the image of a line is a line and in a similarity transformation of space the image of a plane is a plane.

The ratio of the lengths of any two line segments is equal to the ratios of the lengths of their images under a similarity transformation. For let AB and CD be any two segments, and let $A'B'$ and $C'D'$ be their images (the image of a line segment is a line segment by what we said above). Then, for some positive k, $A'B' = kAB$, and $C'D' = kCD$, whence (since $k \neq 0$)

$$\frac{A'B'}{C'D'} = \frac{AB}{CD}.$$

Under a similarity, parallel lines are taken into parallel lines, for the image of a line is a line, and the two image lines can have no point in common, since a similarity is one-one. Similarities also preserve angles. For let A be the vertex of an angle and B and C points on the two arms. Let A', B', C' be the respective images. Then the triangles $A'B'C'$ and ABC are similar, and so they have corresponding angles equal. In particular, a similarity takes perpendicular lines into perpendicular lines.

Suppose that we are given three noncollinear points A, B, C of the plane π and three points A', B', C' of the plane π', which are such that $A'B' = kAB$, $B'C' = kBC$, $C'A' = kCA$. Then there exists one, and only one, similarity of π onto π' that takes A, B, C into A', B', C', respectively.

To prove this, let us choose points B^* and C^* on the rays $A'B'$ and $A'C'$ such that $A'B^* = AB$ and $A'C^* = AC$. Then the triangles ABC and $A'B^*C^*$ are congruent (two sides and included angle), so that $B^*C^* = BC$. By Theorem 8 of Section 5, there exists an orthogonal transformation of π onto π', say β, that takes A, B, C into A', B^*, C^*, respectively. Let us define a transformation γ of the plane π' by making each point M of π' correspond to the point M' for which $A'M' = kA'M$ and make A' correspond to itself. We shall prove in the next section that γ is a similarity transformation of π' with coefficient k, and it is clear that β is a similarity of π onto π' with coefficient 1. So the composite mapping $\gamma\beta$ of π onto π' that takes each point M of π to M' *via* M^* is a similarity with coefficient k of π onto π'. Moreover, it is clear that $\gamma\beta$ takes A, B, C into A', B', C', respectively.

To prove uniqueness, suppose that α and β are two similarities of π onto π', each having the same effect on A, B, and C. Consider the composite mapping $\beta^{-1}\alpha$ of π onto itself. Since α and β have the same coefficient k, β^{-1} has coefficient k^{-1}, and $\beta^{-1}\alpha$ has coefficient 1. So $\beta^{-1}\alpha$ is an orthogonal mapping of π onto itself, and it is clear that it leaves invariant the points A, B, C. By Theorem 8, Section 5, it must be the identity transformation, so $\alpha = \beta$.

Under a similarity, the image of a circle is a circle (we leave the proof to the reader). It is not hard to show that a similarity either preserves the orientation of every triangle (that is, every triangle of the plane has the same orientation as its image) or reverses the orientation of every triangle. We say a similarity transformation is of the first or second kind, depending on which of these cases holds.

It may be shown (just as for orthogonal transformations) that, given two points A, B and two points A', B', there exists precisely one similarity of each kind that takes A, B into A', B', respectively, where A, B are distinct points of a plane π and A', B' are distinct points of a plane π'.

16. Homothetic Transformations

Let O be any point of a given plane and k a given positive number. Then the *homothetic transformation* of the plane with center O and coefficient k is that transformation γ of the plane which leaves O fixed and takes every other point M into the point M' for which $\overrightarrow{OM'} = k\overrightarrow{OM}$ (O, M, M' are collinear, with M and M' on the same side of O). The transformation γ which we introduced on the previous page was a homothetic transformation of the plane π' with center A' and coefficient k.

The set of all homothetic transformations of the plane with a given center O forms a group of transformations. For if α and β are the homothetic transformations with center O and coefficients k_1 and k_2, then $\alpha\beta = \beta\alpha$ is the homothetic transformation with center O and coefficient $k_1 k_2$, and α^{-1} is the homothetic transformation with center O and coefficient $1/k_1$. The identity transformation is the one with coefficient $k = 1$. Note that the identity transformation may be regarded as the homothetic transformation with coefficient 1 and *any* center.

Theorem I. *A homothetic transformation γ with center O and coefficient k is a similarity transformation with coefficient k and is of the first kind.*

Proof. Let A and B be any two distinct points of the plane and A', B' their images. Suppose first that A and B lie on a line through O. If A and B lie on the same side of O, then so do A' and B', and $A'B' = |OB' - OA'| = |kOB - kOA| =$

$k|OB - OA| = kAB$; while if A and B lie on opposite sides of O, $A'B' = OA' + OB' = kOA + kOB = k(OA + OB) = kAB$.

Suppose next that A and B do not lie on a line through O. Then the triangles AOB and $A'OB'$ are similar (they have two pairs of corresponding sides with a common ratio, since $OA' = kOA$ and $OB' = kOB$, and the included angle $AOB = A'OB'$ equal). So the third pair of corresponding sides is also in the same ratio; that is, $A'B' = kAB$. We have thus shown that for any two points A, B, $A'B' = kAB$, and γ is a similarity transformation with coefficient k.

We show next that it is a similarity transformation of the first kind. Let A and B be points not on a line through O and A', B' their images under γ. In the chain of triangles

$$OAB, \quad OA'B, \quad OA'B',$$

both pairs of adjacent triangles have the same orientation, so that the same is true of OAB and $OA'B'$. ▼

It is easy to see that under a homothetic transformation the image of a line is the same or a parallel line, and, moreover, that the sense along a line is preserved; that is, if A, B are distinct points, then the vectors $\overrightarrow{AB}$ and $\overrightarrow{A'B'}$ are parallel and point in the same direction. In fact, we have $\overrightarrow{A'B'} = k\overrightarrow{AB}$.

Conversely, if α is a similarity transformation with coefficient $k \neq 1$ under which each line l is taken into the same or a parallel line l', and, moreover, such that sense is preserved, then α is a homothetic transformation. The hypothesis may be restated in the form: if $\overrightarrow{A'B'} = k\overrightarrow{AB}$ for all A and B and some fixed positive constant $k \neq 1$, then α is a homothetic transformation.

Proof.   If the image of every line is the same line, then α is the identity. For given any point O, choose distinct lines l, m through it. Then O' is the point of intersection of l' and m' and since $l' = l$ and $m' = m$, we have $O' = O$. Suppose then that A and B are two points whose images A', B' do not lie on AB. Since $A'B'$ is parallel but not equal to AB, $ABB'A'$ is not a parallelogram, and therefore AA' and BB' meet in a point O (note that AA' and BB' are well-defined lines, since we may easily see that $A' = A$ or $B' = B$ is impossible). Consider the image of the line OAA' under α. It is the same or a parallel line through the image A' of A, and so it must be the same line. Similarly, OBB' is invariant under α. So the point O of intersection of these lines is invariant under α. Next, the triangles OAB and $OA'B'$ are similar, so that $OA' : OA = OB' : OB = A'B' : AB = k$. Thus $OA' = kOA$ and $OB' = kOB$, and since A and A', and B and B', are on the same side of O, the homothetic transformation with center O and coefficient k, like α, leaves O fixed and takes A to A' and B to B'. By a result in Section 15, this means that α *is* the homothetic transformation with center O. ▼

Note 1. There is nothing to stop us from allowing a *negative* coefficient k in the definition of a homothetic transformation. In this case M is taken to a point M' lying on OM but on the other side of O from where M is located. Thus a homothetic transformation with negative coefficient $-k$ and center O is the product in either order of the (ordinary) homothetic transformation with center O and coefficient k, and the reflection in O. The set of "homothetic" transformations with center O is a commutative group, of which our previous group is a subgroup. We now have Note 2:

Note 2. In our proof of the converse to Theorem 1 we used the fact that $\overrightarrow{A'B'}$ pointed the same way as $\overrightarrow{AB}$ only in order to deduce that A and A' (and B and B') lay on the same side of O. If we allow homothetic transformations to have negative coefficients, we may restate the converse to Theorem 1 as follows:

If α is a transformation such that for some $k \neq 0, 1$ we have $\overrightarrow{A'B'} = k\overrightarrow{AB}$ for all A and B, then α is a homothetic transformation with coefficient k.

This result can be improved still further:

If α is a similarity transformation carrying every vector into a *parallel vector, then* α *is either a homothetic transformation or a translation.*

If α has coefficient k, this amounts to saying that if for every A, B we have $\overrightarrow{A'B'} = \pm k\overrightarrow{AB}$, then we must either always take the $+$ sign, or always take the $-$ sign.

This result suggests that a translation might be regarded as a homothetic transformation with center at infinity and coefficient 1.

Note 3. The use of geometric transformations allows us, in many cases, to give a simple solution of geometric problems that would otherwise be much more difficult. We give an example by proving the following theorems, due to Euler:

Theorem 2. *Let ABC be any triangle, H its orthocenter* (*the point of intersection of its altitudes*), *G its centroid or center of gravity* (*the point of intersection of its medians*), *and O its circumcenter* (*the center of the circumscribed circle S or the point of intersection of the perpendicular bisectors of the sides*). *Then O, G, H are collinear, with G between O and H, and*

$$OG : GH = 1 : 2.$$

In particular, if two of O, G, H coincide, then they all do.

Theorem 3. *The following nine points lie in a circle known as Euler's circle s: the midpoints of the sides of ABC, the bases of its altitudes, and the midpoints of the line segments joining H with the vertices. The center E of s is the midpoint of OH, and its radius is half that of the circumscribed circle.*

Proof. Consider the "homothetic" transformation γ with center G and coefficient $-\frac{1}{2}$. Since G lies a third of the way between each side and the opposite vertex, γ will take A, B, C into the midpoints A', B', C' of the opposite side. Consider the altitude of ABC through A. Its image is a parallel line through the image A' of A, that is, the perpendicular bisector of BC, and similarly for the other altitudes. So the image of the point H of intersection of the altitudes is the point O of intersection of the perpendicular bisectors of the sides. It follows that H and O lie on opposite sides of G and that $OG : GH = 1 : 2$. ▼.

The image of the circumcircle S of ABC is a circle s, whose center is the image of O under γ and which passes through the images A', B', C' of the vertices. Since the image of O is the midpoint E of OH, we see that the circle s through the midpoints of the sides has center E. Since the coefficient of γ (as a similarity transformation) is $\frac{1}{2}$, the radius of s will be half that of S. Now E is equidistant from O and H, and so it is also equidistant from the projections of O and H onto any line, in particular, the sides of ABC. But these projections are just the midpoints of the sides and the bases of the altitudes. Since s with center E passes through the former, it must also pass through the latter.

Consider now the homothetic transformation β with center H and coefficient $\frac{1}{2}$. Just as for γ, the point O is taken into E, and S is taken into a circle with center E and radius half that of S; that is, the circle s. But under β the vertices of ABC go into the midpoints of AH, BH, CH, so that these points lie on s.

The circle s is known as the nine-point, or Euler, circle associated with the triangle ABC. ▼

Note 4. Let A_0, B_0, C_0 be the second points in which the altitudes of ABC meet S. Under β, these points must go into points of s also on the altitudes (since the altitudes pass through the center H of β) and on the same side of H as are A_0, B_0, C_0. So their images are the feet of the altitudes. It follows that BC is the perpendicular bisector of HA_0, and so on; in other words, the reflections of H in the three sides of ABC lie on the circumcircle.

Note 5. In Sections 17 and 18 we shall use the expression "homothetic transformation" to apply only to those transformations which have positive coefficients.

17. Representation of a Similarity Transformation as the Product of a Homothetic Transformation and an Orthogonal Transformation

Theorem I. *Any similarity transformation α with coefficient k can be represented as the product of the homothetic transformation β with coefficient k and prescribed center O, and an orthogonal transformation γ.*

Proof. If $k = 1$, we take the homothetic transformation to be the identity (regarded as the homothetic transformation with center at the given point O and coefficient 1). Let β be the homothetic transformation with coefficient k and center the given point O, and let $\gamma = \beta^{-1}\alpha$. Then $\alpha = \beta\gamma$. By results in Section 14, γ is a similarity transformation with coefficient $k^{-1}k = 1$ and is thus an orthogonal transformation. ▼

We leave it to the reader to show that β and γ are uniquely determined by α and O and the requirement that γ be an orthogonal transformation.

Theorem 2. *Given any similarity transformation α of the plane, exactly one of the following holds:*

(1) *α is an orthogonal transformation.*

(2) *α is not orthogonal and of the first kind. In this case, α has a unique representation $\alpha = \gamma\rho$ such that γ is a homothetic transformation and ρ is a rotation about the center O of γ. Moreover, $\alpha = \rho\gamma$. We allow the special cases where ρ is the rotation through 0 (that is, the identity) or π (that is, the reflection in O).*

(3) *α is not orthogonal and of the second kind. In this case, α has a unique representation $\alpha = \gamma\sigma$ such that γ is a homothetic transformation and σ is the reflection in some line through the center O of γ. Moreover, $\alpha = \sigma\gamma$.*

Proof. Case 1. Let α be a similarity transformation with coefficient k. If $k = 1$, we have the first case. So we assume from now on that $k \neq 1$.

Case 2. Let A be any point, B its image under α, and C the image of B. Then $BC/AB = k$. We distinguish three cases.

i. A, B, C are collinear with B in the middle. There is a unique point O lying on AB, outside the segment AB, such that $OB/OA = k$.

If $k > 1$ then O lies on BA produced in the direction of A and so outside the segment AC. So

$$\frac{OC}{OB} = \frac{OB + BC}{OA + AB} = \frac{kOA + kAB}{OA + AB} = k.$$

If $k < 1$, then O lies on AB produced beyond B, and since

$$\frac{OB}{OA} = \frac{OB}{OB + BA} = k$$

and

$$\frac{BC}{AB} = k,$$

we must have $OB > BC$, and therefore O lies on BC produced beyond C. So

$$\frac{OC}{OB} = \frac{OB - BC}{OA - AB} = \frac{kOA - kAB}{OA - AB} = k.$$

Consider the homothetic transformation γ with center O and coefficient k. Like α, γ takes A into B and B into C, and since α and γ are both of the first kind, $\alpha = \gamma$. To prove part 2 of the theorem, we take ρ to be the identity (rotation through 0 about O).

ii. A, B, C are collinear, and B is not in the middle. Suppose $k > 1$. Choose the point O inside the segment AB for which

$$\frac{OB}{OA} = k.$$

Since $BC/AB = k$, C lies on BA produced beyond A, and therefore

$$\frac{OC}{OB} = \frac{BC - OB}{AB - OA} = \frac{kAB - kOA}{AB - OA} = k.$$

Also A and B, and B and C, lie on opposite sides of O. Let γ be the homothetic transformation with center O and coefficient k, and let σ be the reflection in O. Then, by the usual argument, we see that $\alpha = \gamma\sigma = \sigma\gamma$.

If $k < 1$, consider the inverse transformation α^{-1}. It takes C into B and B into A; B is not in the middle, and the coefficient is > 1. So, by what we have just proved, $\alpha^{-1} = \gamma\sigma = \sigma\gamma$, where γ is a homothetic transformation with coefficient k^{-1}, and σ is the reflection in its center. But then $\alpha = \sigma\gamma^{-1} = \gamma^{-1}\sigma$, where γ^{-1} is a homothetic transformation with coefficient $(k^{-1})^{-1} = k$, and σ is the reflection in its center (which is the same as that of γ).

iii. A, B, C are not collinear. Let S be the circle through A and B tangent to BC at B, and let T be the circle through B and C tangent to AB at B. S and T intersect in two points, one of which is B, the other O, say. Produce CB to a point P and AB to Q. Then $\angle AOB = \angle PBA$ (both are equal to half the arc AB), and similarly $\angle BOC = \angle QBC$. But $\angle PBA = \angle QBC$ (vertically opposite), so that

$$\angle AOB = \angle BOC.$$

Furthermore, $\angle OAB = \angle OBC$. It follows that the triangles OAB and OBC are similar, the scale factor being $BC : AB = k$. Let ρ be the rotation about O through the angle β which takes the ray OA into OB and OB into OC. Then it is clear that $\rho\gamma$, like α, takes A into B and B into C, where γ is the homothetic transformation with coefficient k and center O. Since α and $\rho\gamma$ are both of the first kind, they are equal, and it is clear that also $\rho\gamma = \gamma\rho$.

We now show that if α is a similarity transformation of the first kind, then its representation as the product of a rotation and a homothetic transformation with center at the center of the rotation is unique.

Suppose then that $\alpha = \rho\gamma$, where γ is a rotation about some point O and γ is a homothetic transformation with center O. Then O is fixed under α and is the only such point. For if A also were fixed, then $OA = O'A' = kOA$, so that $k = 1$, contrary to the hypothesis that α is not orthogonal. So if α also can be represented in the form $\rho^*\gamma^*$, where ρ^* and γ^* have the same center, this center must be O.

It follows from

$$\alpha = \rho\gamma = \rho^*\gamma^*$$

that

$$\gamma\gamma^{*-1} = \rho^{-1}\rho^*.$$

But the right side is the product of two rotations about O, so it is itself a rotation about O, and the left side is the product of two homothetic transformations with center O, so it is itself a homothetic transformation with center O. However, a homothetic transformation cannot be a rotation unless it is the identity. Thus $\gamma\gamma^{*-1} = \rho^{-1}\rho^* = \varepsilon$, and $\gamma = \gamma^*$, $\rho = \rho^*$.

Case 3. Let A be any point, B its image, and C the image of B. Then $BC/AB = k$. We distinguish cases, as before.

    i. A, B, C all lie on a line l, with B in the middle.

We have already shown (Case 2,i) that there exists a homothetic transformation γ with center O on l taking A to B and B to C. Let σ be the reflection in l. Then σ leaves the points of l invariant, and so it also takes A to B and B to C. By the usual argument, $\alpha = \gamma\sigma = \sigma\gamma$, and this is a representation in the required form.

    ii. A, B, C are collinear, with B not in the middle. In this case, we know that there is a homothetic transformation γ with coefficient k and center O on l, such that $\sigma\gamma$ takes A into B and B into C, where σ is the reflection in O. Let m be the perpendicular to l through O, and let σ' be the reflection in m. Then σ' has the same effect on the points of l as does σ. Thus $\sigma'\gamma$ takes A into B and B into C, and, being of the second kind, it must be α. Also $\alpha = \gamma\sigma'$.

    iii. A, B, C are not collinear. Choose points P and Q on the line segments AB and BC, respectively, such that $BP : PA = CQ : QB = k$. Let A^* and B^* be the reflections of A and B in the line $l = PQ$. A and C lie on the same side of l, which is the opposite side from B. Thus on one side of l lie A^* and B and on the other A, B^*, and C. The ratio of the distances to l from B and A^* is $k \neq 1$, so that A^*B intersects l in some point O lying outside the segments A^*B, since A^* and B are on the same side of l.

Since

$$\frac{CQ}{QB} = k,$$

we have

$$QB = \frac{BC}{k+1} = \frac{k}{k+1} \, AB,$$

and since

$$\frac{BP}{PA} = k,$$

we have

$$PB = \frac{k}{k+1} \cdot AB,$$

so that $BQ = PB$, and $\angle BPQ = \angle BQP = \beta$, say. Since B and B^* are symmetrically opposite l, $\angle B^*PQ = \beta$, so that PB^* is parallel to $BQ = BC$ (alternate angles). Since A^*, P, B^* are the images of A, P, B under the reflection in l, they are collinear. Thus A^*B^* is parallel to BC.

We now show that B^*C passes through O. Let C' be the point of intersection of OB^* and BC (they are not parallel, since then OB^* would also be parallel to A^*B^*). Since A^*B^* is parallel to BC, $C'Q : QB = B^*P : PA^*$. But $B^*P : PA^* = PB : PA = k$. Thus $C'Q : QB = k = CQ : QB$, so that C' coincides with C. Now the triangles OA^*B^* and OBC are similar (since they have the same angle at O and parallel bases), so that

$$\frac{OB}{OA^*} = \frac{BC}{A^*B^*} = \frac{BC}{AB} = k.$$

Let σ be the reflection in l. It takes A and B into A^* and B^* respectively. The homothetic transformation γ with center O and coefficient k takes A^* to B and, therefore, also takes B^*

into C (for the image D of B^* must lie on OB^* and also be such that BD is parallel to A^*B^*). Thus $\gamma\sigma = \sigma\gamma$, like α, takes A into B and B and C, and, since both are of the second kind, we have

$$\alpha = \gamma\sigma = \sigma\gamma.$$

To prove the uniqueness of this representation, note that the center O of γ is the only point invariant under α. So if also $\alpha = \sigma^*\gamma^*$, where γ^* is a homothetic transformation with center O^* and σ^* the reflection in a line through O^*, then we must have $O^* = O$.

Since

$$\alpha = \sigma\gamma = \sigma^*\gamma^*,$$

we have

$$\sigma^{*-1}\sigma = \gamma^*\gamma^{-1}.$$

But the left side, the product of reflections in two lines through O, is a rotation about O, while the right side is a homothetic transformation with center O. This means that both sides are the identity, so that $\sigma^* = \sigma$, $\gamma^* = \gamma$. ▼

18. Similarity Transformations of the Plane in Coordinates

18.1. HOMOTHETIC TRANSFORMATIONS

Let γ be the homothetic transformation with center O and coefficient k. We introduce a system of rectangular coordinates with origin at O. Let (x, y) be the coordinates of a point M of the plane and (x', y') those of its image M' under γ. Drop perpendiculars MP and MQ from M onto the x and y axes and perpendiculars $M'P'$ and $M'Q'$ from M' (Fig. 44). Then

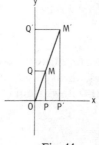

$$\frac{OM'}{OM} = \frac{OP'}{OP} = \frac{OQ'}{OQ} = k. \qquad (3)$$

Fig. 44

So

$$OP' = kOP,$$

$$OQ' = kOQ.$$

Now P and P' lie on the same side of the same ray Ox through O, and similarly for Q and Q'. It follows that

$$x' = kx,$$

$$y' = ky.$$

18.2. THE GENERAL CASE

Let α be a similarity transformation with coefficient k. We introduce rectangular coordinates with origin at any point O. By Theorem 1 of the last section, we may write $\alpha = \omega\gamma$, where γ is the homothetic transformation with center O and coefficient k, and ω is an orthogonal transformation.

By Section 18.1, γ takes the point $M(x, y)$ into the point $M^*(x^*, y^*)$, where

$$x^* = kx,$$

$$y^* = ky. \tag{1}$$

If α is of the first kind, so is ω, and, by Eq. (4) in Section 10.5, if $\omega(M^*) = M'(x', y')$,

$$x' = x^* \cos \beta - y^* \sin \beta + a,$$

$$y' = x^* \sin \beta + y^* \cos \beta + b. \tag{2}$$

Here (a, b) are the coordinates of the image O' of O, and β is the angle through which every vector is rotated by α (or ω).

It follows from (1) and (2) that

$$x' = k(x \cos \beta - y \sin \beta) + a,$$

$$y' = k(x \sin \beta + y \cos \beta) + b.$$

If α is of the second kind, then so is ω and, as before, we have

$$x' = k(x \cos 2\gamma + y \sin 2\gamma) + a,$$

$$y' = k(x \sin 2\gamma - y \cos 2\gamma) + b,$$

where (a, b) are the coordinates of the image O' of O under α, and γ is the angle that the axis of any reflection σ, such that $\omega = \sigma\tau$ for some translation τ, makes with the x axis. Or we may say that 2γ is the angle between Ox and its image under α or ω.

19. Similarity Transformations in Space

Similarity transformations of space are defined just as for the plane. Under them, lines go into lines, the order of points along lines is preserved, planes go into planes, the images of two parallel lines or planes are two parallel lines or planes, angles between lines or planes are preserved, and the ratio between the lengths of segments is preserved.

If A, B, C, D are any four noncoplanar points, and A', B', C', D' are four points such that the tetrahedra $ABCD$ and $A'B'C'D'$ are similar, then there exists a unique similarity transformation taking A, B, C, D into A', B', C', D', respectively, and the coefficient of this transformation is the ratio between any pair of corresponding sides of the two tetrahedra (for example, $A'B' : AB$). Just as for plane transformations, similarity transformations of space can be divided into those of the first and second kinds.

If A, B, C are three noncollinear points and A', B', C' are three points such that the triangles ABC and $A'B'C'$ are similar, then there exists a unique similarity transformation of the first kind and a unique one of the second kind, taking A, B, C into A', B', C', respectively. These two transformations have the same coefficient $k = B'C' : BC$.

The set of all similarity transformations of space forms a group, of which the orthogonal group of space is a subgroup.

A homothetic transformation of space is defined in the same way as a plane homothetic transformation. A given similarity can be represented in the form $\gamma\beta$, where γ is a homothetic transformation with prescribed center O, and β is an orthogonal transformation of space.

Any similarity transformation α of space either is an orthogonal transformation or can be represented uniquely as the product of a homothetic transformation γ and a rotation ρ about an axis l passing through the center O of γ, if α is of the first kind, or as a product $\gamma\rho\sigma$ where γ and ρ satisfy the conditions above and σ is the reflection in the plane through O perpendicular to l, if α is of the second kind. These transformations can be taken in any order. In particular, a similarity transformation of space with coefficient $k \neq 1$ has a unique fixed point.

If we introduce rectangular coordinates in space, then a given similarity transformation α with coefficient k is specified in coordinates by a system of equations of the following form:

$$x' = k(a_{11}x + a_{12}y + a_{13}z) + a,$$
$$y' = k(a_{21}x + a_{22}y + a_{23}z) + b, \qquad (1)$$
$$z' = k(a_{31}x + a_{32}y + a_{33}z) + c,$$

where (x', y', z') are the coordinates of the image M' of the point M with coordinates (x, y, z). The image O' of O has coefficients (a, b, c), and the a_{ij} are the direction cosines of the angles that the images of the three coordinate axes make with the coordinate axes. In particular, the a_{ij} satisfy Eqs. (1) and (2) of Section 13. We may prove (1) above exactly as we proved the corresponding result for the plane in Section 18, by using the results of Section 13. As a particular case of (1), the analytic expression for the homothetic transformation with center O and coefficient k is

$$x' = kx,$$
$$y' = ky,$$
$$z' = kz.$$

We may use (1) to prove that a similarity transformation of space with coefficient $k \neq 1$ has a unique fixed point. The coordinates of a fixed point $M(x, y, z)$ must satisfy (1) when we substitute x for x', etc. Thus we have

$$(a_{11}k - 1)x + a_{12}ky + a_{13}kz + a = 0,$$

$$a_{21}kx + (a_{22}k - 1)y + a_{23}kz + b = 0,$$

$$a_{31}kx + a_{32}ky + (a_{33}k - 1)z + c = 0.$$

To show that this system of equations has a unique solution it is sufficient (and necessary) to show that the determinant associated with it is nonzero, so that

$$\begin{vmatrix} a_{11}k - 1 & a_{12}k & a_{13}k \\ a_{21}k & a_{22}k - 1 & a_{23}k \\ a_{31}k & a_{32}k & a_{33}k - 1 \end{vmatrix} \neq 0.$$

But this determinant is zero if and only if there exist numbers p, q, r such that

$$a_{11}p + a_{12}q + a_{13}r = \frac{1}{k}\,p,$$

$$a_{21}p + a_{22}q + a_{23}r = \frac{1}{k}\,q, \tag{2}$$

$$a_{31}p + a_{32}q + a_{33}r = \frac{1}{k}\,r.$$

Now the left-hand sides of these equations are the coordinates of the image of the point $P(p, q, r)$ under the orthogonal transformation α whose analytic expression is given by (1) of Section 13 (with $a = b = c = 0$). If this is the point P', then we must have $OP' = OP$. But the coordinates of P' are given by the right-hand side of (2), and we see from them that $OP' = k^{-1}OP$. So the determinant cannot be zero if $k \neq 1$, and the system (1) above has a unique solution.

We could establish in exactly the same way that a similarity transformation of the plane has exactly one fixed point; having done so, Theorem 2 of Section 17 becomes very easy, and the result on the representation of a similarity transformation of space as a product of elementary transformations (given above) becomes equally easy. For a direct proof (not using analytic methods to establish the existence of a fixed point), see Jacques Hadamard, "Leçons de géométrie élémentaire," Vol. I, p. 142, A. Colin, Paris, 1898.

We may define similarity transformations in the obvious manner for spaces of higher dimensions than three, and all the obvious analogs of previous results continue to hold. In particular, the analytic expression for such a transformation is the obvious generalization of (1), subject to conditions generalizing (2) in Section 13. A similarity transformation with coefficient $k \neq 1$ of a space of any number of dimensions has exactly one fixed point.

CHAPTER IV

Affine Transformations

In the previous chapter we considered the simplest geometric transformations— those that preserve shape. The group of similarity transformations of the plane is a subgroup of a group of more general transformations, that preserve collinearity and parallelism, but not, in general, lengths of segments, sizes of angles, or areas. These are the affine transformations.

20. Definition of Affine Mappings and Transformations of the Plane

Definition. A one-one mapping α of a plane π onto a plane π' is said to be *affine*, provided that the images of any three collinear points are themselves collinear.

Theorem. *Under an affine mapping, any three noncollinear points have noncollinear images.*

Proof. Let α be an affine mapping of the plane π onto the plane π', and suppose that the images under α of three non-collinear points P, Q, R are collinear points P', Q', R'. We show that every point M of π has its image M' on $l' = P'Q'R'$. Let m be any line through M except MP, and suppose it meets PQ and PR in the (distinct) points A, B (Fig. 45).

Since P, A, Q are collinear, the image A' of A lies on $P'Q' = l'$, and similarly the image B' of B lies on l'. Since α is one-one, A' and B' are distinct, and since M lies on AB, M' lies on $A'B' = l'$. Thus every point of π has its image on l', contradicting the fact that α is onto. ▼

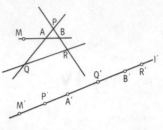

Fig. 45

Corollary. *The inverse of an affine mapping is itself affine.*

An affine mapping of π onto itself is called an affine transformation of π. The orthogonal and similarity transformations considered in the previous chapters serve as simple examples of affine transformations. It follows from the definition that the product of two affine transformations of π is itself an affine transformation of π, and from the corollary it follows that the inverse of an affine transformation of π is also one. Thus the set of all affine transformations of the plane is a group. The identity of this group is the identity transformation.

The group of similarity transformations of the plane is a subgroup of this group, and the group of orthogonal transformations is another.

Note. It was pointed out to the authors by Professor Smirnov that we do not have to specify that α be one-one in our definition of an affine mapping α of one plane onto another, since this property can be proved from the other assumptions.

21. Examples of Affine Transformations and Mappings of a Plane

21.1. SKEW REFLECTION

Under orthogonal mappings, both lengths of segments and angles between segments are preserved. Under similarity transformations, angles are preserved but not lengths (unless the transformation is orthogonal). The simplest example of an affine transformation in which both lengths and angles change is provided by skew reflection.

Suppose we are given distinct lines Ox and Oy in the plane (Fig. 46). Given any point M, we draw the parallel through M to Oy to meet Ox in P and produce it to M', where $PM' = MP$. Let α be the transformation of the plane that takes each point M into M' (in particular, α is the identity on Ox). We call α the *skew reflection* in Ox parallel to Oy. Skew reflection is an affine transformation, for it is clearly one-one and onto. Suppose A, B, C are three collinear points of π. If they lie on a line l parallel to Ox, then the image of l under α is its (ordinary) reflection in Ox, so that the images of A, B, C are collinear (Fig. 47); if not, suppose that l meets Ox in P. Then l' is the line PA' (Figs. 48 and 49). This is also true in the special case where l is parallel to (or coincides with) Oy: the image of l in this case is l itself. A skew reflection is a similarity transformation only if Ox and Oy are perpendicular, in which case it is the

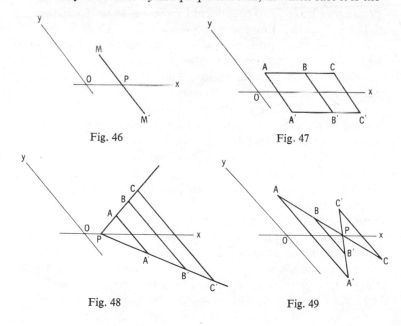

Fig. 46

Fig. 47

Fig. 48

Fig. 49

(ordinary) reflection in Ox. We leave it to the reader to check that otherwise α preserves neither all lengths nor all angles.

If we take Ox and Oy as (skew) coordinate axes, then the skew reflection in Ox relative to Oy is given coordinatewise by

$$x' = x; \qquad y' = -y.$$

21.2. COMPRESSION

Let k be a positive number and l a given line of the plane π. Let M be any point of π and MP the perpendicular from M to l

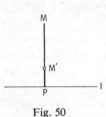

Fig. 50

(Fig. 50). Let M' be the point such that $\overrightarrow{M'P} = k\overrightarrow{MP}$. Thus M and M' lie on MP, on the same side of l. In particular, if M lies on l, then $M' = M$. Let α be the transformation of the plane that takes each point M into M'. We call α the *compression with axis l and coefficient k*. It is clear that α has the inverse transformation β, where β is the compression with axis l and coefficient $1/k$. So α is a transformation.

If $k < 1$ we have a proper compression, in which every point not on l is moved closer to it; if $k > 1$ we have a stretching, in which points not on l move further away from it. If $k = 1$ we have the identity transformation. Thus the identity transformation may be regarded as the compression with any axis l and coefficient 1. The set of all compressions with a given axis (including the identity) forms a group of transformations. Just as for homothetic transformations, we may allow k to be negative in our definition of a "compression." In this case M and M' lie on opposite sides of l. The "compression" with negative coefficient $-k$ is the product in either order of the ordinary compression, with coefficient k and axis l, and the reflection in l (compare Section 16).

To show that a compression is an affine mapping, it is enough to show that the image of a line m is a line (since we know already that it is one-one and onto). If m is perpendicular to l, this is clear. Otherwise, let A, B, C be three points of m, and let A_0, B_0, C_0 be the feet of the perpendiculars from them to l.

Then A', B', C' lie on A_0A, B_0B, C_0C, respectively, and are such that

$$\frac{A'A_0}{AA_0} = \frac{B'B_0}{BB_0} = \frac{C'C_0}{CC_0} = k.$$

It is clear from these equalities that A', B', C' are collinear. In fact, they lie on the line through the point of intersection of m with l and with slope k times the slope of m (if l and m are parallel, m' is parallel to both of them).

Thus compression with respect to a given axis is an affine transformation.

A compression is determined by the axis and a pair of corresponding points M, M' not lying on it. Moreover, the construction of the image N' of a point N may be made geometrically. If N does not lie on MM' and MN is not parallel to the axis l, suppose that MN meets l in P. Then the image N' of N is the point of intersection of PM' and the perpendicular from N to l. If N lies on MM', first carry out the construction for a point N_0 as above and then the construction for N, using N_0 and N_0' instead of M and M'. (We can choose N_0 arbitrarily, except that it should not lie on MM' or on the parallel to l through M or N.) If MN is parallel to l, we leave the construction to the reader. This construction suggests the following geometric curiosity. Suppose that we are given M, M' and l, as in Fig. 51, and suppose that Q and Q', are two other points related to M and M' in the same way as N and N', are. Then NQ and $N'Q'$ must meet on l (or both be parallel to it). The reader might like to supply a direct geometric proof.

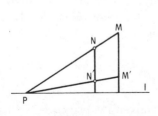

Fig. 51

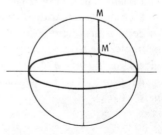

Fig. 52

Under a compression a circle is transformed into an ellipse. Indeed, an ellipse is often defined to be the image of a circle under a compression with a diameter of the circle as axis. The ratio of the minor to the major axis is precisely the coefficient of the compression (if it is a compression rather than a stretching). See Fig. 52.

In Fig. 53, we show a square grating and its image under the compression with axis l and coefficient $k = \frac{1}{2}$.

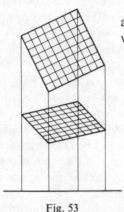

Fig. 53

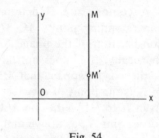

Fig. 54

If we take the line l for the x axis and any perpendicular to it for the y axis, then a compression is given coordinatewise by

$$x' = x,$$
$$y' = ky,$$

where (x, y) are the coordinates of a general point M and (x', y') are those of its image M' under the compression with axis Ox and coefficient k (Fig. 54).

A compression transformation may be used in the solution of certain problems in geometric constructions. Consider, for example, the following problem: Find the point or points on a given line p such that the sum of the distances from it to two given points F_1, F_2 is the length of a given line segment m $(> F_1F_2)$.

Solution.   The set of all those points of the plane, the sum of whose distances from F_1 and F_2 is equal to m, is the ellipse with foci F_1 and F_2 and major axis m. Let O be the midpoint of F_1F_2, and let A_1 and A_2 be the points of F_1F_2 for which

$$OA_1 = OA_2 = \frac{m}{2}.$$

Construct the right triangle OBF_1 in which $F_1B = OA_1$. Then OB is the minor axis of the ellipse with foci F_1 and F_2 and major axis OA.

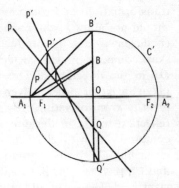

Fig. 55

Mark off on the ray OB the point B' such that $OB' = OA_1$.

Consider the "compression" of the plane with axis A_1A_2 that takes B into B'. It will take our ellipse into the circle C' with radius OA_1 and center O, and the line p into a line p', which we can construct (as on the previous page). See Fig. 55.

Let P' and Q' be the points in which p' meets the circle C. Draw parallels through P' and Q' to OB to meet p in P and Q. Then P and Q are the required points. If p' is tangent to C, there is only one point, and if p' lies outside C, then there is no solution. To prove the correctness of the construction, we need merely note that P and Q are the inverse images of P' and Q' under our "compression" and must therefore lie on the ellipse, since P' and Q' lie on its image, the circle.

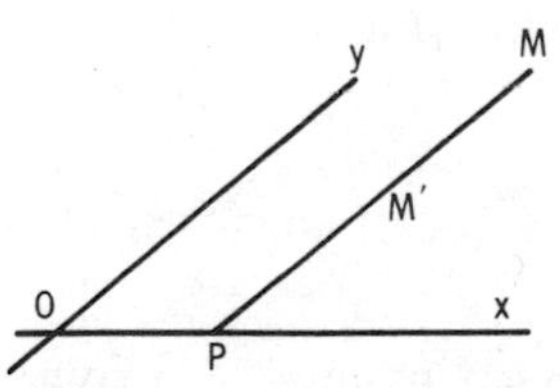

21.3. Skew Compression

Suppose we are given two lines Ox, Oy (not necessarily perpendicular), and a positive number k (Fig. 56). Through each point M of the plane draw the line parallel to Oy, and let it meet Ox in P. Let M' be the point

Fig. 56

(of PM) such that $\overrightarrow{M'P} = k\overrightarrow{MP}$. In particular, if M lies on Ox, $M' = M$. Let α be the mapping of the plane that takes each point M into M'. Then α is called the *skew compression* onto the axis Ox in the direction of Oy and with coefficient k.

We leave it to the reader to show that a skew compression is an affine transformation of the plane. As with homothetic transformations and compressions, there is no reason why we should not allow $k < 0$. Each skew compression with negative coefficient $-k$ is the product of the corresponding ordinary skew compression with coefficient k and the skew reflection in Ox in the direction of Oy; moreover, the product may be taken in either order. Given Ox and Oy, if $k = 1$, α is the identity transformation, whereas if $k = -1$, it is the skew reflection in Ox in the direction of Oy. The set of all skew compressions with given axis Ox and in the direction of a given line Oy forms a group. If α and β have coefficients k_1 and k_2, then $\alpha\beta = \beta\alpha$ has coefficient $k_1 k_2$, while α^{-1} has coefficient k_1^{-1}. The set of all skew compressions (with Ox and Oy given) in which we also allow those with negative coefficient is a larger group and is also commutative.

A skew compression is determined by its axis and the image of any point M not on it. Moreover, given M and M' (and the axis l), we may construct the image N' of any point N geometrically.

If Ox and Oy are taken as (skew) coordinate axes, then α is given in coordinates by

$$x' = x,$$

$$y' = ky,$$

where (x, y) are the coordinates of a point M and (x', y') those of its image M' under α.

21.4. HYPERBOLIC ROTATION

Let Ox and Oy be distinct lines intersecting in O. For some positive number k, let α be the skew compression onto Ox, parallel to Oy and with coefficient k, and β the skew compression onto Oy, parallel to Ox and with coefficient $1/k$.

The product transformation $\gamma = \alpha\beta = \beta\alpha$ is the product of two affine transformations and so is itself an affine transformation. It is called a *hyperbolic rotation.*

The reason for this name is as follows: The image of a point $M(x, y)$ (where we take the coordinates in the system with axes Ox and Oy) is the point $M'(x', y')$, where

$$x' = \frac{1}{k}\, x, \qquad y' = ky.$$

Thus

$$x'y' = xy.$$

If the point M lies on the hyperbola

$$xy = C,$$

its image M' lies on the same hyperbola, since $x'y' = xy = C$. We thus have the following situation: we are given a point O and a system of conics—the set of all those conics with the lines Ox and Oy as asymptotes (and center O). There is exactly one such conic through each point M of the plane. Then the transformation γ takes each point M onto another point M' on the same conic, where the position of M' (given M) is determined by the "coefficient" k of γ. Consider now the analogous situation with an ordinary rotation: we are given a point O and the set of all those conics that are circles with center O. There is exactly one such conic through each point M of the plane. Then a rotation ρ with center O and angle of rotation θ takes each point M onto another point M' of the same conic of the system (that is, the same circle center O), where the position of M' (given M) is determined by the "coefficient" θ of ρ. We may make the analogy still closer if we allow complex coordinates, for then circles with center O are precisely those conics whose asymptotes are a certain pair of (imaginary) lines intersecting in O.

In Fig. 57, we show a circle inscribed in a square and its

image under the hyperbolic rotations with $k = 2$ and $k = \frac{1}{2}$ and mutually perpendicular axes Ox and Oy.

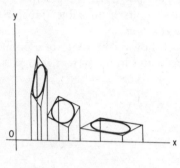

Fig. 57

Under a hyperbolic rotation, the points lying on Ox and Oy go into points on the same lines. The point O of intersection of Ox and Oy is invariant.

Under a hyperbolic rotation, the areas of figures are preserved. For, under compression onto Ox with coefficient k, all areas are multiplied by k, while, under the compression onto Oy, all areas are multiplied by $1/k$. (See Section 28.)

Hyperbolic transformations are connected with Lobachevskian (or *hyperbolic*) geometry (as opposed to Euclidean geometry). They are also met with in the theory of relativity.

21.5. ELLIPTIC ROTATION

Suppose we are given the line l and a positive number k. Let α be the compression onto l with coefficient k and ρ the rotation about a point O of l through an angle φ. Consider the transformation $\gamma = \alpha\rho\alpha^{-1}$. It will take a point M of the plane into M' via P and P' (Fig. 58). The transformation γ is the product of three affine transformations, so it is itself an affine transformation. It is called an *elliptic rotation*.

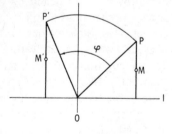

Fig. 58

The reason for calling the transformation γ an elliptic rotation is that γ leaves invariant all the ellipses with center O and major axis l whose ellipticity is k, where by ellipticity we mean the ratio between the semi-axes of the ellipse. Thus, just as for rotations and hyperbolic rotations, we have the following situation: we are given a point O and a system of conics—the set of all ellipses with given (major or minor) axis l, with ellipticity the given number k, and with center O. There is exactly one such conic through each point M of the plane. The transformation γ takes M into a point M' of the same conic of the system, where the position of M' (given M) is determined by the "coefficient" φ of γ. The specification of k for an elliptic rotation corresponds to the specification of the slant of Oy in a hyperbolic rotation. To make the analogy closer, we may note that the set of ellipses described above is just that set of conics that has a certain pair of (imaginary) lines through O as asymptotes.

To prove that an ellipse of the system is invariant under γ, consider that its image under α is a circle with center O, that this circle is invariant under ρ, and that α^{-1} takes it back into the ellipse again.

An elliptic rotation is determined by the point O, the line l, and any pair of corresponding points M, M' ($\neq O$). For there exists a unique ellipse K through M and M' with center O and major axis l. Let C be the circle whose radius is the major semi-axis of K, and whose center is O, and let k be the coefficient of the compression onto l that takes K into C. Let the images of M and M' under this compression be P and P', and let φ be the oriented angle between the rays OP and OP'. Then k and φ determine the elliptic rotation satisfying the given conditions. We may prove, similarly, that a hyperbolic rotation is determined by O, Ox and any pair of corresponding points M, M' not lying on Ox.

21.6. SHEAR

Let us introduce a system of Cartesian coordinates (not necessarily rectangular) in the plane, the coordinate axes being Ox and Oy. Let α be that mapping of the plane which takes a point $M(x, y)$ of the plane onto the point $M'(x', y')$, where

$$x' = x + ky,$$

$$y' = y.$$

The geometric meaning of such a mapping (which we call a shear) is as follows: each point M goes into a point M' on the same horizontal line (line parallel or coincident with Ox). Furthermore, since the coordinates of the vector $\overrightarrow{MM'}$ are $x' - x = ky$ and $y' - y = 0$, the absolute value of this vector is $|k|\,|y|$. Thus, each point M is transferred horizontally a distance proportionate to its distance from the x axis, since $|y|$ is proportionate to this distance. If $ky > 0$, then the direction of $\overrightarrow{MM'}$ is the positive direction of Ox, whereas if $ky < 0$, $\overrightarrow{MM'}$ is pointed in the negative direction of the x axis. Thus if $k > 0$, points lying above Ox are moved to the right, but points below it are moved to the left, and vice versa if $k < 0$.

Under a shear, every point of the x axis remains fixed. A shear is determined completely by the axis Ox and any pair of corresponding points M, M' (not lying on Ox). With this information, the image under the shear of a point N of the plane may be obtained geometrically as illustrated in Fig. 59.

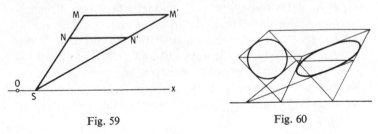

Fig. 59   Fig. 60

In Fig. 60 we show a circle inscribed in a square and its image under a shear.

We now show that a shear is an affine transformation. In a given system of coordinates, the inverse of the shear with coefficient k is the shear with coefficient $-k$. Thus a shear is one-one and onto. It remains to show that collinear points go into collinear points.

Let $A(x_1, y_1)$, $B(x_2, y_2)$, $C(x_3, y_3)$ be three collinear points, and let $A'(x_1', y_1')$, and so on, be their images under a shear. Then

$$x_1' = x_1 + ky_1, \qquad y_1' = y_1;$$
$$x_2' = x_2 + ky_2, \qquad y_2' = y_2;$$
$$x_3' = x_3 = ky_3, \qquad y_3' = y_3.$$

Since A, B, C are collinear,

$$\begin{vmatrix} x_1 & y_1 & 1 \\ x_2 & y_2 & 1 \\ x_3 & y_3 & 1 \end{vmatrix} = 0;$$

furthermore,

$$\begin{vmatrix} x_1' & y_1' & 1 \\ x_2' & y_2' & 1 \\ x_3' & y_3' & 1 \end{vmatrix} = \begin{vmatrix} x_1 + ky_1 & y_1 & 1 \\ x_2 + ky_2 & y_2 & 1 \\ x_3 + ky_3 & y_3 & 1 \end{vmatrix} = \begin{vmatrix} x_1 & y_1 & 1 \\ x_2 & y_2 & 1 \\ x_3 & y_3 & 1 \end{vmatrix} = 0.$$

It follows that A', B', C' are also collinear.

A shear preserves areas. To prove this, it is enough to show it for triangles (the general case may then be obtained by a limiting argument). Let A, B, C be three points, A', B', C' their images, and let the coordinates be as above. Then

$$\text{area } \triangle A'B'C' = \frac{1}{2}\begin{vmatrix} x_1' & y_1' & 1 \\ x_2' & y_2' & 1 \\ x_3' & y_3' & 1 \end{vmatrix}$$

$$= \frac{1}{2}\begin{vmatrix} x_1 + ky_1 & y_1 & 1 \\ x_2 + ky_2 & y_2 & 1 \\ x_3 + ky_3 & y_3 & 1 \end{vmatrix} = \frac{1}{2}\begin{vmatrix} x_1 & y_1 & 1 \\ x_2 & y_2 & 1 \\ x_3 & y_3 & 1 \end{vmatrix}$$

$$= \text{area } \triangle ABC.$$

The set of all shears defined in a given coordinate system by the equations at the beginning of this subsection (for various k) forms a group of transformations. For if α is the shear with coefficient k and β the shear with coefficient k', then $\alpha\beta = \beta\alpha$ is the shear with coefficient $k + k'$, and α^{-1} is the shear with coefficient $-k$. The identity of this group is the identity transformation, which may be regarded as that shear of the given system which has coefficient $k = 0$.

It is true, similarly, that the set of all hyperbolic rotations with given axes Ox and Oy (and various coefficients k) forms a group of transformations. If α is the hyperbolic rotation (with these axes) with coefficient k and β the hyperbolic rotation with k', then $\alpha\beta$ is the hyperbolic rotation with these axes and coefficient kk', and α^{-1} is that with coefficient k^{-1}. Thus this group (like the group of all shears in a given coordinate system) is commutative. Similarly, for given ellipticity k and a given center O and axis l, the set of all elliptic rotations forms a commutative group. The product of the elliptic rotation with coefficient φ_1 and φ_2 is the one with coefficient $\varphi_1 + \varphi_2$, and the inverse of the elliptic rotation with coefficient φ is the one with coefficient $-\varphi$. The identity element of this group is the identity transformation of the plane, which may be regarded as the elliptic rotation with coefficient 0.

21.7. PARALLEL PROJECTION

A very important form of affine transformation is parallel projection, a special case of which is orthogonal projection. Orthogonal projection is the fundamental method of representing solid figures in a plane. For example, the plans of a house will show front elevation, side elevation and plan, these being orthogonal projections of the house in three mutually perpendicular directions (followed by a scaling down, of course!) Orthogonal projection is fundamental in the study of descriptive geometry (Monge's method).

Let π and π^* be any two planes, and p a line not parallel to either of them. We make correspond to each point M of π the point M^* of π such that MM^* is parallel to p. This is a one-one mapping of π onto π^*, for it has the inverse defined in exactly the same way, with the roles of π and π^* interchanged. Moreover, the image of a line in π is a line in π^*. Thus the mapping is affine. This mapping is called the *parallel projection* in the direction of p of π onto π^*. If the planes are parallel (and only in this case), the mapping is orthogonal; if the planes intersect on the line l, then every point of l is invariant under the mapping.

Let us note that a parallel projection of a circle is an ellipse. Conversely, a given ellipse may be obtained as the parallel projection of a circle of given radius if and only if this radius lies between the major and minor semi-axis of the ellipse.

Suppose now that π and π^* intersect in the line l. We rotate π^* about l until it comes into coincidence with π. Let M' be the point of π into which M^* is taken by this rotation, and let α be the transformation that takes M into M'. It is clear that α is an affine transformation of π leaving l pointwise invariant. It is called an affinity, and l is called its axis.

Theorem I.   *Any affine transformation α of the plane in which every point of some given line l remains invariant (each point of l coincides with its image) is an affinity with axis l.*

Proof.   Let A be any point not on l, and A' its image under α. We rotate π about l through an arbitrary angle and denote by A^* the point into which A' is taken. Consider the parallel projection of the plane π onto the rotated plane π^* in the direction AA^*, followed by the rotation about l of π^* back onto π. This transformation γ is an affinity having the same effect as α on A and on every point of l. We show below (Section 25) that there is a unique affine transformation taking three given noncollinear points of π into three other noncollinear points. Assuming this, we deduce $\gamma = \alpha$, since A does not lie on l. ▼

The proof above shows that an affinity α does not determine the plane π^* and the line l: for *any* plane π^* passing through the axis l of α, there exists a line p such that α is associated with the parallel projection from π onto π^* in the direction of p.

Theorem 1 shows that an affinity may be defined intrinsically as an affine transformation ρ of the plane π leaving some line l of π pointwise invariant. By "intrinsically" we mean that this definition refers only to the *action* of ρ, not to any mechanism (such as projection and rotation of planes in space) that may be available to *realize* ρ. In particular, this definition does not take us outside the plane π on which ρ is defined.

Our next result shows how any affinity (defined intrinsically) can be represented in terms of the elementary types of affine transformation that were introduced in Section 21.

Theorem 2. *Let ρ be an affinity with axis l taking A (not on l) to A'. (1) If AA' is parallel to l, ρ is a shear; (2) otherwise ρ is a skew compression onto l in the direction of AA'.*

We allow a skew compression to have a negative coefficient (see Section 21.3).

Proof. (1) If the directed distance from AA' to l is y, and $AA' = ky$, then ρ is the shear σ with coefficient k and axes l and a line perpendicular to l. For ρ and σ have the same effect on A and on every point of l, and we may now appeal to the theorem of Section 25 below.

(2) Let AA' meet l in P. Set $k = \overrightarrow{A'P} : \overrightarrow{AP}$. Then we may show similarly that ρ equals the skew compression τ with coefficient k onto l in the direction of AA'. ▼

It may be noted that we only needed shears with perpendicular axes. The reader is invited to investigate what this theorem says about shears fixing $l = Ox$ but with the other axis Oy not perpendicular to Ox (see Section 21.6).

21.8. ORTHOGONAL PROJECTION

Let π and π^* be two planes, not perpendicular. Let p be any line perpendicular to π^*. Let α be the parallel projection of π onto π^* in the direction of p. Then α is called the *orthogonal projection* of π onto π^*. As a special case of a parallel projection, it is an affine mapping.

If π and π^* are parallel, α is an orthogonal mapping; if they intersect in the line l, then the affinity generated by the orthogonal projection α of π onto π^* is either a compression (not a skew compression) against l or a compression followed by reflection, both with axis l.

22. Properties of Affine Mappings

Theorem I. *Under an affine mapping α of a plane π onto a plane π' the image of any line l of π is a line l' of π'.*

Proof. Let l be a line of π, and let A, B be two distinct points on it. Then the images A' and B' of A and B under α will be distinct (since α is one-one). Let l' be the line $A'B'$. If C is any point of l, then since A, B, C are collinear, A', B', C' are collinear. Thus C' lies on l', and the image of l under α is a part of l' (α maps l *into* l'). Let C' be any point of l'. Then the inverse image C of C' under α must lie on l, since the inverse of an affine mapping is also an affine mapping. Thus α maps l *onto* l'. ▼

Theorem 2. *Under an affine mapping α of π onto π', parallel lines go into parallel lines and intersecting lines into intersecting lines. Furthermore, the point of intersection of two lines l, m goes into the point of intersection of their images l', m'.*

Proof. Let a and b be two parallel lines of π. Their images under α are two lines a', b' (by Theorem 1). If a' and b' intersect in a point M', then the (unique) inverse image M of M' would have to lie on both a and b, which is impossible. Thus a' and b' are parallel.

Suppose now a and b intersect in M. Then the image M' of M must lie on both a' and b'; that is, a' and b' intersect in M'. ▼

When we were developing the theory of orthogonal and similarity transformations, we went on from theorems such as 1 and 2 above to show that the image of a line segment was another segment and that the ratio in which a point divides a line segment was invariant.

It is true that the same two properties hold of affine mapping (although, as with similarity transformations, the image of a segment need not be an *equal* segment). However, in this case, a proof of the two properties is by no means simple. For a long time it was even considered that these properties do not, in fact, follow from the definitions we gave at the beginning of this chapter for an affine mapping and that we can have them only by further restricting the definition; for instance, by requiring affine mappings to be continuous (that is, intuitively, that they take points that are close together into points that are close together) or requiring them to preserve the order of three collinear points (that is, if B lies between A and C on the line AC, then B' lies between A' and C' on $A'C'$). This was the approach taken by the founders of the theory of projective and affine transformations—Poncelet, Möbius, Chasles, and others. It was only in 1880 that the French geometer Darboux found that no such additional condition is necessary, since these conditions, as well as the two properties we wished to prove, can all be deduced from the postulates for an affine transformation that we have given.

In his article "The fundamental theorem of projective geometry," *Math. Ann.* **17**, 55–61 (1880), Darboux proved that cross ratio is preserved by projective transformations, the method of proof being essentially to reduce to a proof of the preservation of ordinary ratio (along a line) under affine mappings.

Before giving an account of these questions, we prove a simple theorem, which is derived immediately from the definition of an affine mapping.

Theorem 3. *Under an affine mapping, the image of the midpoint of a segment is the midpoint of the image segment.*

Proof.   Let C be the midpoint of the segment AB. Draw any two distinct lines through A, neither of them being AB. Draw

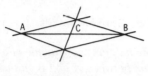

the lines through B parallel to them. The four lines we obtain form a parallelogram, the point of intersection of whose diagonals is C (Fig. 61). By Theorems 1 and 2, the image of this parallelogram under α is another parallelogram

Fig. 61

whose diagonals bisect in the image C' of C. But this means that C' is the midpoint of $A'B'$. ▼

Corollary. *If the points $D_1, D_2, \ldots, D_{n-1}$ divide the segment AB into n equal parts, then their images $D_1', D_2', \ldots, D'_{n-1}$ under an affine mapping divide the segment $A'B'$ (where A' and B' are the images under the mapping of A and B) into n equal parts.*

For we have $AD = D_1 D_2 = \cdots = D_{n-1} B$. Thus D_1 is the midpoint of AD_2, so that D_1' is the midpoint of $A'D_2'$; that is, $A'D_1' = D_1'D_2'$, and so on. ▼

Suppose now that A and B are fixed points on a line l, and A', B' are their image on a line l' under an affine mapping. Let us take A as the origin on l and B the point with coordinate 1 (that is, AB is the unit segment on l). Then let us take A' as the origin on l' and B' as the unit point on l'. It follows at once from the corollary that each point of the segment AB that has a rational coordinate r goes into the point of $A'B'$ with coordinate r. It also follows from the corollary that points on l (not necessarily inside the segment AB) with rational coordinates have as images the points of l' with the same rational coordinates. Thus (in terms of a given origin and unit of lengths), an affine mapping has all the nice properties we require of it as far as the *rational* points of the line are concerned—order is preserved, ratio of segments, continuity. It would be a very weird mapping that dealt so nicely with the rational points but took the irrational ones elsewhere than into their "proper" places. This is the reason the earlier geometers felt impelled to impose some such condition as continuity in their definition of an affine mapping.

23. Darboux's Lemma and its Consequences

Darboux's Lemma.   *Under an affine mapping, the image of a point C of the segment AB (that is, lying between A and B on the line AB) is a point C' of the segment A'B' (that is, lying between A' and B' and on the line A'B', where A' and B' are the images under the mapping of A and B).*

Proof.   It is sufficient to show that an exterior point of AB is mapped into an exterior point of $A'B'$ (that is, a point of $A'B'$ lying outside the segment $A'B'$). For, if an interior point of AB is mapped into an exterior point of $A'B'$, then, under the inverse map, an exterior point of $A'B'$ is mapped into an interior point of AB. So suppose that A and B are any two distinct points of π and C a point of AB lying outside the segment AB. Since the vectors $\overrightarrow{AC}$ and $\overrightarrow{CB}$ have opposite directions, their ratio is negative, and we may write

$$\frac{\overrightarrow{AC}}{\overrightarrow{CB}} = -\lambda^2$$

for some real number λ. Let P and Q be the points of AB (P being inside the segment AB and Q outside it) for which

$$\frac{\overrightarrow{AP}}{\overrightarrow{PB}} = \lambda, \qquad \frac{\overrightarrow{AQ}}{\overrightarrow{QB}} = -\lambda.$$

Then C is the midpoint of the segment PQ. For if we assign coordinates to the points of $l = AB$, taking A for origin and B for unit point, then

$$x_P = \frac{\lambda}{1 + \lambda}, \qquad x_Q = \frac{-\lambda}{1 - \lambda}.$$

So the center C' of PQ has the coordinate

$$x = \frac{1}{2}(x_P + x_Q) = \frac{1}{2}\left(\frac{\lambda}{1+\lambda} - \frac{\lambda}{1-\lambda}\right) = \frac{-\lambda^2}{1-\lambda^2}.$$

But this is just the coordinate of C, so that C and C' coincide.

We draw through A and B two parallel lines (not being the line AB) and mark off on the line through A points M and N such that $AN = AM$. Let QM and QN meet the line through B in K and L (Fig. 62). Then $BL = BK$, $AN : BL = \lambda$, and NK and LM intersect in P.

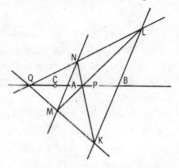

Under the affine mapping, the parallel lines go into parallel lines, the midpoints of the segments into the midpoints of the corresponding segments, and collinear points into collinear points. Thus the transformed figure is of the same form, and, in particular, if one of P', Q' is interior to $A'B'$, then the other is exterior. Note that in the argument we now give we do not assume anything about which of P' and Q' is interior to $A'B'$. Suppose, for example, that Q' is interior; then P' is exterior, and we have

Fig. 62

$$\frac{\overrightarrow{A'P'}}{\overrightarrow{P'B'}} = -\lambda', \qquad \frac{\overrightarrow{A'Q'}}{\overrightarrow{Q'B'}} = \lambda'.$$

for some real λ'. But C' is the center of $P'Q'$ and therefore divides $A'B'$ externally in the ratio $-\lambda'^{12}$ and so lies outside the segment $A'B'$. ▼

Corollary.   *Under an affine mapping, the image of a segment is a segment.*

For, as we have shown, every point of the segment AB is mapped into a point of the segment $A'B'$, and since the inverse

of an affine mapping is affine, the inverse image of a point of
the segment $A'B'$ is a point of the segment AB.

Corollary.   *Under an affine transformation, the interior
points of a triangle (parallelogram) are taken into the interior
points of a triangle (parallelogram).*

Suppose that ABC is a triangle. Its image (that is, the image
of its three sides) will be a triangle. (We leave the proof to the
reader.) Let M be any point inside ABC, and let AM meet BC
in D. Then D is an interior point of BC, and M is an interior
point of AD. It follows that D' is an interior point of $B'C'$, and
M' is an interior point of $A'D'$. It follows at once from this that
M' is interior to $A'B'C'$.

The image of the boundary of a parallelogram is certainly a
parallelogram. If M is an interior point of a parallelogram,
then it is either the center of the parallelogram or an interior
point of one of the four triangles obtained by taking two adjacent
sides of the parallelogram and one diagonal. In either case, the
proof that the image of M is an interior point of the image
parallelogram is simple.

It follows from Corollary 2 that the image of a bounded set
under an affine mapping is itself bounded. For a bounded set
may be surrounded by a triangle; that is, it may be made to
consist entirely of interior points of the triangle, and its image
must then consist entirely of interior points of the image
triangle and must therefore also be bounded.

24.   Invariance of Length Ratios
Under Affine Mappings

Theorem.   *Under an affine map, the point C dividing the
segment AB (internally or externally) in the ratio λ is taken into
the point C' dividing the segment $A'B'$ (in the usual notation) in
the same ratio λ.*

This theorem may be formulated more concisely by saying that ratios are preserved by affine mappings.

Proof. If λ is rational, the result follows from the corollary to Theorem 3 (Section 22). If λ is irrational, suppose, for the sake of contradiction, that

$$\frac{A'C'}{C'B'} > \frac{AC}{CB}$$

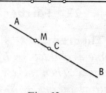

(Fig. 63). Choose the point D' of $A'B'$ for which

$$\frac{A'D'}{D'B'} = \frac{AC}{CB};$$

Fig. 63

then D' does not coincide with C'. So we may choose a point M' between D' and C' whose coordinate (in terms of the unit $A'B'$ and measured from A') is rational. Since $A'D'/D'B' < A'C'/C'B'$, C' lies between D' and B', therefore C' also lies between M' and B'. So C lies between M and B, and

$$\frac{AC}{CB} = \frac{A'D'}{A'B'} < \frac{A'M'}{M'B'} = \frac{AM}{MB},$$

which is a contradiction.

If C lies outside the segment AB (our proof assumed it did not), then B, say, lies between A and C, and, by what we have already proved,

$$\frac{AB}{BC} = \frac{A'B'}{B'C'},$$

whence

$$\frac{AB}{BC} + 1 = \frac{A'B'}{B'C'} + 1,$$

$$\frac{AC}{CB} = \frac{AB + BC}{BC} = \frac{A'B' + B'C'}{B'C'} = \frac{A'C'}{C'B'}.$$

Since C and C' lie outside AB and $A'B'$, respectively, both these ratios are negative, so that

$$\frac{\overrightarrow{AC}}{\overrightarrow{CB}} = \frac{\overrightarrow{A'C'}}{\overrightarrow{C'B'}},$$

as required. ▼

25. Further Properties of Affine Mappings

Theorem. *Let A, B, C be any three noncollinear points of the plane π, and let A', B', C' be any three noncollinear points of the plane π'. Then there exists one and only one affine mapping of π onto π' taking A, B, C into A', B', C', respectively.*

Proof. We introduce in π an affine system of coordinates, taking C as the origin, CA and CB as the coordinate axes, and A and B as the unit points on the respective axes. We introduce a system of coordinates in π' similarly (origin C', coordinate axes $C'A'$ and $C'B'$, and so on).

We construct a mapping of π onto π' as follows: let M be any point of π, and (x, y) its coordinates in the given system. Let M' be the point of π' having the *same* coordinates (x, y) as M, in the coordinate system for π'. Then we make M correspond to M'. This mapping α is one-one and onto, for it has the inverse defined in the same way with the roles of π and π' interchanged.

To show that α is affine, it is enough to show that the image of a line l in π is a line l' of $\pi.'$ Now a line l in π has an equation of the form $Px + Qy + R = 0$, where P, Q, R are real numbers, and not both P and Q are zero. That is to say, a point $M(x, y)$ lies on l if and only if its coordinates satisfy this equation. Let l' be the line of π' having the same equation. Then M' lies on l' if and only if M lies on l (since the coordinates are the same and the equation is the same). Thus the image of l under α is l', and α is an affine mapping.

We show now that any affine mapping β taking A, B, C into A', B', C', respectively, must coincide with α. Let $M(x, y)$ be any point of π. Let the parallels through M to CB and CA meet

CA and CB, respectively, in P and Q. Then the coordinates of M are given by

$$x = \frac{\overrightarrow{CP}}{\overrightarrow{CA}}, \qquad y = \frac{\overrightarrow{CQ}}{\overrightarrow{CB}}.$$

Let P' and Q' be the images of P and Q under β. By the invariance of ratio (Section 24),

$$\frac{\overrightarrow{C'P'}}{\overrightarrow{C'A'}} = \frac{\overrightarrow{CP}}{\overrightarrow{CA}} = x, \qquad \frac{\overrightarrow{C'Q'}}{\overrightarrow{C'B'}} = \frac{\overrightarrow{CQ}}{\overrightarrow{CB}} = y.$$

Since parallelism is preserved by the affine mapping β, $M'P'$ is parallel to $C'B'$, and $M'Q'$ is parallel to $C'A'$. It follows that the coordinates of M' are (x, y). Thus β has the same effect on any point M of π as does α, so that $\beta = \alpha$. ▼

Corollary. *If, under an affine transformation α of π, three noncollinear points A, B, C remain fixed, then α is the identity.*

For α has the same effect as ε on three noncollinear points, so that, by the uniqueness theorem above, it must be ε.

The proof we gave is constructive, in the sense that given A, B, C in π and their images A', B', C' under an affine transformation α (where A, B, C are noncollinear), our proof shows how to give a construction for the image of any point M. Draw parallels MP and MQ through M to the coordinate axes. Through C' draw parallels λ and μ to CA and CB. Draw parallels through A, P, B, Q to CC', to meet λ (in the case of A and P) and μ (in the case of B and Q) in A_0, P_0, B_0, Q_0, respectively. Through P_0 and Q_0 draw parallels to A_0A' and B_0B', respectively, to meet CA' and CB', respectively, in P' and Q'. Finally, draw parallels through P' and Q' to $C'B'$ and $C'A'$, respectively. Their point M' of intersection is the required image of M (Fig, 64). To prove this, it is enough to show that the coordinates of P' and Q' (in the coordinate system $C'A'B'$) are the same as those of P and Q in the coordinate system CAB.

Now the x coordinate of P is $CP : CA = C'P_0 : C'A_0 = C'P' : C'A'$, which is the x coordinate of P'—and similarly for Q and Q'.

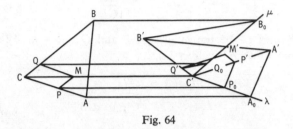

Fig. 64

Note that in this construction we did not need to do anything except draw the line through two given points and the parallel through a given point to a given line.

26. Representation of any Affine Transformation as a Product of Affine Transformations of the Simplest Types

Lemma I. *Any affine transformation of the plane can be represented as the product of a similarity transformation and an affinity. (We recollect that an affinity is any affine transformation leaving some line pointwise invariant.)*

Proof. Let A, B, C be any three noncollinear points of π, and let A', B', C' be their images under the affine transformation α. Let C^* be a point of π for which the triangles ABC^* and $A'B'C'$ are similar. Let ρ be the affinity with axis AB that takes C into C^*, and let σ be the similarity transformation that takes A, B, C^* into A', B', C', respectively. Then the product, like α, takes A, B, C into A', B', C', respectively, so that, by the uniqueness theorem (Section 25), the two are equal. ▼

Note that there are two possible choices of C, one on the same side of AB as C, and one on the other. We may therefore restrict the affinity to be a shear or skew compression with positive coefficient, or alternately, to be a skew compression with negative coefficient (see Theorem 2, Section 21.7). Alternately we may restrict σ to be of the first or of the second kind. There is, therefore, no uniqueness to this representation.

Lemma 2.   *Given any affinity ρ of the plane π, and a point A of π, we may find two perpendicular lines of π through A whose images are also perpendicular.*

Proof.   If AA' is perpendicular to *l*, we may take the lines to be the parallel and the perpendicular through A to *l*.

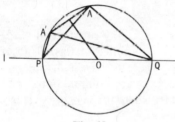

Fig. 65

If not, let O be the point of intersection of *l* and the perpendicular bisector of AA'. Let C be the circle with center O that passes through A and A', and let it meet *l* in P and Q (Fig. 65). Since P and Q are invariant under ρ, the lines AP and AQ go into the lines $A'P$ and $A'Q$, and since PQ is a diameter of C, both these pairs of lines are perpendicular. ▼

Theorem.   *Any affine transformation of the plane is the product of two compressions in perpendicular directions and an orthogonal transformation.*

Proof.   Let α be any affine transformation. By Lemma 1, we may write $\alpha = \sigma\rho$, where σ is a similarity and ρ an affinity. By Lemma 2, there is a pair of perpendicular lines whose image under ρ is another pair of perpendicular lines. Since similarity transformations preserve angles, the image of this pair under σ is also a pair of perpendicular lines. Thus, given an affine transformation α, we may find perpendicular lines Ox and Oy whose images under α are perpendicular lines $O'x'$, $O'y'$.

Choose points A and B on Ox and Oy, respectively (neither being the point O), and let their images under α be A' and B'. Let ω be the orthogonal transformation taking O into O' and A and B into points A^* and B^* of the rays $O'A'$ and $O'B'$. Let ξ_1 be the compression onto $O'x'$ taking B^* into B', and ξ_2 the compression onto $O'y'$ taking A^* into A'. Then the product transformation $\xi_1\xi_2\omega$ takes O, A, B into O', A', B', respectively, and so equals α, by the theorem in Section 25. ▼

Corollary I.   *Any affine mapping α of a plane π onto a plane π' can be represented as the product of an orthogonal mapping of π onto π', followed by two compressions onto perpendicular axes in π'.*

For we may write $\alpha = \beta\omega$, where ω is any orthogonal mapping of π onto π', and $\beta = \alpha\omega^{-1}$ is an affine transformation of π'. By the theorem, $\beta = \xi_1\xi_2\omega'$, where ω' is an orthogonal transformation of π', and ξ_1 and ξ_2 are compressions onto orthogonal axes. Then $\alpha = \xi_1\xi_2\omega^*$, where $\omega^* = \omega'\omega$ is clearly an orthogonal mapping of π onto π'.

Corollary 2.   *Any affine transformation can be represented as the product of a compression and a similarity transformation.*

This corollary is an improvement on Lemma 1 above. To prove it, note that in the representation of the theorem we may replace the compression ξ_2 onto $O'y'$ (with coefficient k_2) by the homothetic transformation γ with center O and coefficient k_2, and the compression ξ_1 onto $O'x'$ (with coefficient k_1) by the compression ξ onto $O'x'$ with coefficient k_1/k_2. For γ has the same effect on every point of $O'x'$ as ξ_2, and ξ and ξ_1 leave $O'x'$ pointwise invariant, while $\xi\gamma$ clearly has the same effect as $\xi_1\xi_2$ on every point of $O'y'$. Thus, by the theorem of Section 25, $\xi_1\xi_2 = \xi\gamma$. But then $\alpha = \xi_1\xi_2\omega = \xi\gamma\omega = \xi\sigma$, where σ is clearly a similarity transformation.

27. Noninvariance of Lengths of Segments under Affine Mappings

Under an affine map of one plane onto another, the lengths of segments do not, in general, remain invariant, and segments in different directions change their lengths in different ratios.

Corollary 1 of Section 26 allows us to give some details on this change of length, and from it we will deduce further facts on the representation given in the theorem.

Let α be an affine mapping of π onto π', and suppose that in some representation $\alpha = \xi_1 \xi_2 \omega$ (as in the theorem above) the coefficient of compression of ξ_1 is k_1, and that of ξ_2 is k_2. Since $\xi_1 \xi_2 = \xi_2 \xi_1$, we may assume, without loss of generality, that $k_1 \le k_2$. Then we have the following:

Theorem I.   (a) *If AB is any segment in π (and $B \neq A$), and $A'B'$ is its image under α in π', then*

$$k_1 \le \frac{A'B'}{AB} \le k_2 . \tag{1}$$

(b) *Parallel segments change their length in the same ratio. That is, if $AB \| CD$, then*

$$\frac{A'B'}{AB} = \frac{C'D'}{CD} .$$

(c) *If $k_1 \neq k_2$, then nonparallel segments change their lengths in different ratios.*

Proof.   Let Ox and Oy be the axes of ξ_1 and ξ_2. Then their images in π' are perpendicular axes $O'x'$ and $O'y'$. Suppose first that AB is parallel to Oy. Then $A'B' = k_2 AB$, and (a) and (b) are satisfied.

Suppose next that AB has slope λ. Draw parallels through A and B to Oy and Ox, respectively, to meet in X. The images of these lines are parallel to $O'y'$ and $O'x'$, and so perpendicular to each other. Suppose $XB = q$. Then

$$AB^2 = q^2 \lambda^2 + q^2,$$

and

$$A'B'^2 = A'X'^2 + X'B'^2 = k_1^2 q^2 \lambda^2 + k_2^2 q^2.$$

Thus

$$\left(\frac{A'B'}{AB}\right)^2 = \frac{k_1^2 \lambda^2 + k_2^2}{\lambda^2 + 1}. \qquad (2)$$

Part (a) now follows from (2) and the relations

$$k_1^2 = \frac{k_1^2 \lambda^2 + k_1^2}{\lambda^2 + 1} \qquad k_2^2 = \frac{k_2^2 \lambda^2 + k_2^2}{\lambda^2 + 1}.$$

Since (2) is independent of the position of AB and of its length (and depends only on its slope λ), (b) is also clear.

(c) follows from the algebraic fact that, if $|k_1| \neq |k_2|$ and $|\lambda| \neq |\mu|$, then

$$\frac{k_1^2 \lambda^2 + k_2^2}{\lambda^2 + 1} \neq \frac{k_1^2 \mu^2 + k_2^2}{\mu^2 + 1}.$$

The special case where AB is parallel to Oy is also easy. ▼

Theorem 2. *Let α be an affine mapping of π onto π'. Then either* (1) *α is a similarity, or* (2) *in any representation $\alpha = \xi_1 \xi_2 \omega$ (where ω is an orthogonal mapping of π onto π' and ξ_1 and ξ_2 are compressions onto perpendicular axes in π'), ξ_1 and ξ_2 are determined up to translations (or are completely determined by ω).*

Proof. Let $\alpha = \xi_1 \xi_2 \omega$ be one representation of α in the required form. If $k_1 = k_2$, then $\xi_1 \xi_2$ is the homothetic transformation with coefficient $k = k_1 = k_2$ and center the point of intersection of the axes of ξ_1 and ξ_2. In this case, there is no uniqueness, since any pair of perpendicular axes through O would serve as the axes of ξ_1' and ξ_2' in a representation $\alpha = \xi_1' \xi_2' \omega$.

If $k_1 \neq k_2$, and $\alpha = \xi_1' \xi_2' \omega'$ is any representation of α in the required form, then k_1' and k_2' are determined by (1) above to be k_1 and k_2 (in some order—we may assume $k_1' \leq k_2'$ to remove this ambiguity). The direction of the axes of ξ_1' and ξ_2' are determined by (c) as the unique directions in which the extreme values k_1 and k_2 are assumed by $A'B'/AB$. If the axis of ξ_1', for example, is the line $y = a$ (in a coordinate system in which the axes Ox and Oy of ξ_1 and ξ_2 are taken as coordinate axes), then $\xi_1' = \xi_1 \tau$, where τ is the translation a distance

$$a\,(1 - k_1)/k_1$$

in the positive direction of Oy.

If ω is given, then $\alpha\omega^{-1}$ has the unique fixed point O (the point of intersection of the axes of ξ_1 and ξ_2). This means that the axes of ξ_1' and ξ_2' must pass through O. We have thus fixed the axes and the coefficients of ξ_1' and ξ_2', and this determines them completely as ξ_1 and ξ_2. ▼

Corollary. *The numbers k_1 and k_2 associated with an affine mapping α are independent of the particular representation used. They are called (in a slightly different context) the characteristic roots of α. If $k_1 \neq k_2$, the directions of the axes of ξ_1 and ξ_2 are uniquely determined; these directions are called the principal directions, and the axes are called the principal axes of α.*

In this chapter we shall refer to k_1 and k_2 as the *coefficients of compression* of α.

28. The Change in Area under an Affine Mapping of One Plane onto Another

Theorem. *Under an affine mapping α of one plane onto another, all areas are changed in the same ratio, this ratio being $k_1 k_2$, where k_1 and k_2 are the coefficients of compression of α.*

Proof. We use the representation of α given in Section 26. Under ω areas do not change, so it is enough to show that if k is the coefficient of a compression against a line l, and F' is the image under this compression of any given figure F, then

$$s' = ks,$$

where s, s' are the areas of F, F'.

If F is a square with one side parallel to l, this is clear. In the general case, we may cover F with a network of squares whose area exceeds that of F by less than any assigned quantity ε. Then the image will be a network of rectangles covering F' and therefore having an area at least that of F'. Thus

$$k(s + \varepsilon) \geq s' \qquad \text{for any } \varepsilon, \text{ so that} \quad ks \geq s'.$$

On repeating the argument with the inverse mapping (which is also a compression onto l, and which takes F' into F), we see that

$$(1/k)s' \geq s.$$

So

$$s' = ks$$

as required. ▼

29. An Application of Affine Transformations to the Investigation of Properties of the Ellipse

In order to establish certain properties of geometric figures, it is often useful to subject the figure to a suitable affine transformation, study the transformed figure, and from *its* properties deduce those of the original figure.

In Section 29 we use this method to establish certain geometric properties of the ellipse.

An ellipse K may be defined as the image of a circle C under a compression of the plane onto a diameter l of C.

Lemma I.   *In the definition above, we may take the compression to be proper.*

For let K be the image of the circle C under the compression ξ onto the diameter l of C and with coefficient $k > 1$.

Let m be the diameter of C perpendicular to l, and let C' be the circle with the same center O as C and with radius k times as great. We assert that K is the image of C' under a proper compression onto m.

Let ξ' be the compression onto m with coefficient k, and let N be any point of K, M its inverse image under ξ, and P its image under ξ'. We show that P lies on C', which will show that K is included in the image under ξ'^{-1} of C'.

Now $\xi'\xi = \gamma$ is the homothetic transformation with center O and coefficient k. For it is clear that γ and $\xi'\xi$ have the same effect on every point of l and m. Thus $\xi'\xi(M) = \xi'(N) = P$, where $P = \gamma(M)$ is the point of C' lying on the ray OM (Fig. 66). Thus K is included in the image under ξ'^{-1} of C', and ξ'^{-1} is the compression with axis m and coefficient $k^{-1} < 1$.

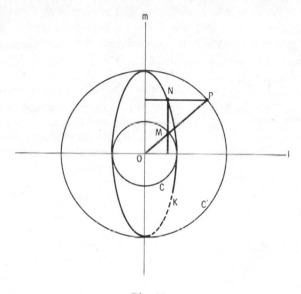

Fig. 66

To show that every point of C' maps onto K, we make the same argument with the roles of C and C' reversed and the inverse mappings ξ^{-1}, ξ'^{-1}. This argument will show that the image N of any point P of C' under ξ'^{-1} has image under ξ^{-1} a point M of C, that is, is the image under ξ of M, and so is a point of K, be definition.

Lemma 2. *Any ellipse is the orthogonal projection of a circle.*

For let K be the image of a circle C with center O and radius a under the compression ξ onto a diameter l of C and with coefficient $k = b/a < 1$ (by Lemma 1).

Let π' be the plane through l making an angle $\theta = \arccos (b/a)$ with π, and let C' be the circle in π' with center O and radius a. Then K is the image of C' under the orthogonal projection α of π' onto π.

For let A be any point of C', and suppose that the perpendicular through A to l meets it in X. Let $\alpha(A) = B$. Then XB is perpendicular to l, and if it meets C in D, then clearly $AX = XD$. But $BX = AX \cos \theta = XD \cdot k$. So B is the image of D under ξ, and therefore lies on K.

Conversely, if B lies on K, and $\xi(D) = B$, let DB meet l in X, and suppose that the perpendicular through X to l in π' meets C' in A. Then we leave it to the reader to show that $\alpha(A) = B$.

Theorem I. *An ellipse has a unique center of symmetry. (A center of symmetry for a geometric figure X is defined to be any point O such that $\alpha(X) = X$, where α is the reflection in O.)*

Proof. The center O of a circle is a center of symmetry. Since, under an affine map, the center of a segment is taken into the center of the image segment (Theorem 3, Section 22), we conclude that the image O' of O under the compression ξ that takes C into the given ellipse K is a center of symmetry of K. If K had a second center of symmetry, then its inverse image under ξ would be a second center of symmetry of C (as the inverse of an affine map is affine). But this is impossible, since the diameter of C passing through this point would have two distinct centers. ▼

Let us note that a bounded figure cannot have more than one center of symmetry anyway. For let A and B be two centers of symmetry of the bounded plane figure K. Introduce coordinate axes by taking A as origin, AB as X-axis, and AB as unit of length.

Let $P = P_1$, Q_1, P_2, Q_2, ..., P_n, Q_n, ... be the points obtained from a given point P of K by successive reflection in A and B alternately. If $P = P(u, v)$, then $Q_1 = (-u, -v)$, $P_2 = (u + 2, v)$, $Q_2 = (-u - 2, -v)$, ..., $P_n = (u + n, v)$, $Q_n = (-u - n, -v)$, ... Thus these points form an unbounded set. Since they all lie in K, K is unbounded.

Theorem 2. *The locus of the midpoints of a system of parallel chords of an ellipse K is a chord of K passing through its center.*

Proof. As usual, let C be a circle of which K is the image under a compression ξ.

Since ξ^{-1} is an affine transformation, it preserves parallelism. Thus the system of parallel chords of K is taken into a system of parallel chords of C. Since affine transformations preserve midpoints, the image of the locus mentioned in the theorem is the locus of the centers of the parallel chords of the circle. But this locus is the diameter of C perpendicular to these chords; that is, it is a straight line passing through the center of C. But then its image under ξ is a line passing through the center of K, and this line is the required locus. ▼

Note. The converse is also true; that is, a closed convex curve with the property that the locus of the midpoints of a system of parallel chords is a straight line must be an ellipse.

The proof of this is rather difficult, and we do not give it.

A line containing the locus of the midpoints of a system of parallel chords of an ellipse is called a *diameter* of the ellipse, and it is said to be *conjugate* to every chord of the system.

We have already shown that every diameter of an ellipse passes through its center. Conversely, any chord of an ellipse that passes through its center is a diameter.

For it is the image of some diameter of C and is therefore the diameter conjugate to the images of the chords of *C* perpendicular to this diameter.

A diameter d_1 is said to be conjugate to the diameter d_2 if d_1 bisects all the chords parallel to d_2.

Theorem 3.   *Let d_1 and d_2 be diameters of an ellipse K. If d_1 is conjugate to d_2, then d_2 is conjugate to d_1.*

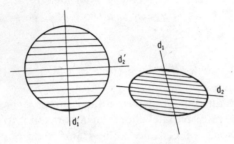

Fig. 67

Proof.   We know that d_1 bisects the chords parallel to d_2 (Fig. 67). Let d_1' and d_2' be the diameters of the circle *C* that are mapped onto d_1 and d_2 under the compression that maps *C* into *K*. Then d_1' and d_2' are perpendicular, since d_2' is parallel to the system of chords bisected by d_1. Thus d_1' is parallel to the system of chords bisected by d_2' and the compression transfers the same property to d_1 and d_2. So d_2 is conjugate to d_1. ▼

We may speak in the future of two *conjugate diameters*, meaning diameters each of which is conjugate to the other. Theorem 3 says that if one diameter is conjugate to another, then the two are conjugate.

Theorem 4.   *If an ellipse is not a circle, it has precisely two axes of symmetry. Moreover these are perpendicular. (An axis of symmetry for a configuration K is any line l such that $\alpha(K) = K$, where α is the reflection in l.)*

Proof. It is clear that the axis *l* of the compression taking *C* into *K* is an axis of symmetry and that the diameter perpendicular to it is another.

Any pair of conjugate diameters of an ellipse is obtained from some pair of perpendicular diameters of the circle. But under the compression, a pair of perpendicular diameters (other than the pair one of which is *l*) goes into conjugate diameters of *K* which are *not* perpendicular (see Fig. 68 for a "proof without words"). So the centers of a system of parallel chords not parallel or perpendicular to *l* lie on a diameter not perpendicular to these chords.

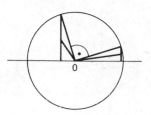

Fig. 68

Suppose now that *n* is an axis of symmetry. Then *n* bisects every chord of *K* perpendicular to it and so must be *l* or the diameter perpendicular to *l*.

We call any segment joining the center of *K* with a point on *K* a *radius* of *K*. We call radii lying on conjugate diameters *conjugate radii*. The radii lying on the axes of symmetry are called the *semi-axes*, and the two axes of symmetry are called the *major axis* (the longer one) and the *minor axis*.

Theorem 5. (Apollonius' First Theorem). *Let K be an ellipse and let r_1, r_2 be conjugate radii. Then the parallelogram on r_1 and r_2 is equal in area to the rectangle on the two semi-axes.*

(A parallelogram is said to be *on* two lines if they are adjacent sides of it.)

Proof. The square on two perpendicular radii of *C* has the same area whatever the radii. In particular, the inverse image of the parallelogram on r_1 and r_2 under the compression ξ that takes *C* into *K* is the square on two perpendicular radii and so has the same area as the inverse image of the rectangle on the two semi-axes. Since ξ changes all areas in the same ratio (Section 28), the original parallelogram and rectangle also have the same area. ▼

Theorem 6. (Apollonius' Second Theorem). *The sum of the squares of the lengths of two conjugate radii is equal to the sum of the squares of the lengths of the semi-axes:*

$$a'^2 + b'^2 = a^2 + b^2.$$

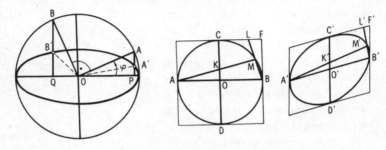

Fig. 69   Fig. 70

Proof. With the configuration of Fig. 69, we have

$$A'P = AP \frac{b}{a} = OA \sin \varphi \frac{b}{a} = b \sin \varphi;$$

$$OP = OA \cos \varphi = a \cos \varphi;$$

$$B'Q = BQ \frac{b}{a} = OB \sin\left(\frac{\pi}{2} + \varphi\right) \frac{b}{a} = b \cos \varphi;$$

$$OQ = \left|OB \cos\left(\frac{\pi}{2} + \varphi\right)\right| = a \sin \varphi.$$

Hence

$$a'^2 + b'^2 = OA'^2 + OB'^2 = OP^2 + PA'^2 + OQ^2 + QB'^2$$
$$= b^2 \sin^2 \varphi + a^2 \cos^2 \varphi + b^2 \cos^2 \varphi + a^2 \sin^2 \varphi$$
$$= a^2 + b^2. \quad \blacktriangledown$$

To conclude this section, we give a construction for any number of points on an ellipse, given only two conjugate radii. Consider the first figure of Fig. 70. We have the circle C

inscribed in a square, and choose any point M on it. With K, L, and so on, as shown, we have

$$OK = FL, \qquad KC = LC.$$

For in the triangles AOK and BFL, we have the angles at A and B equal and $AO = FB$ by construction. Thus the triangles are congruent, and $OK = FL$. It follows that

$$\frac{OK}{KC} = \frac{FL}{LC},$$

Now consider the image under the compression that takes OC and OB into the given conjugate radii of the ellipse. Since ratios are unaltered under an affine mapping, we have

$$\frac{O'K'}{K'C'} = \frac{F'L'}{L'C'}.$$

So, given only the conjugate radii $O'B'$ and $O'C'$, we obtain an arbitrary point M' as follows: mark off the points A' and D' on $B'O'$ and $C'O'$, so that $A'O' = O'B'$ and $D'O' = O'C'$. $A'B'$ and $C'D'$ are conjugate diameters of K. Draw parallels through A' and B' to $C'D'$ and through C' and D' to $A'B'$. Choose any point K' of, say, $O'C'$. Suppose that the parallel to $O'F'$ through K' meets $C'F'$ in L'. Then $A'K'$ and $B'L'$ meet in a point M' of the ellipse. To obtain points in the other quadrants, carry out the corresponding construction when K' is chosen on $O'A'$, $O'D'$, or $O'B'$.

30. Affine Transformations in Coordinates

We introduce in the plane a system of coordinates xOy with origin O and unit points E_1 and E_2.

We make correspond to each point $M(x, y)$ of the plane the point $M'(x', y')$ whose coordinates are expressed, in terms of those of M, by the relations

$$x' = a_1 x + b_2 y + c_1,$$
$$y' = a_2 x + b_2 y + c_2, \tag{1}$$

where

$$\Delta = \begin{vmatrix} a_1 & b_1 \\ a_2 & b_2 \end{vmatrix} = a_1 b_2 - b_1 a_2 \neq 0. \tag{2}$$

We will show that this is an affine transformation of the plane.

First, the mapping is well defined. For given a pair of numbers x, y (1) associates with them a unique pair of numbers x', y'. Thus a given point $M(x, y)$ has associated with it the unique point $M'(x', y')$. Because of the condition (2), the mapping is one-one. For this condition guarantees that the system (1) has a *unique* solution for x and y when x' and y' are given. The mapping is onto, because (2) guarantees that the system of Eq. (1) *does have* a solution for any given x', y'.

To show that the mapping is affine, it is enough now to check the collinearity property. Let l be a given line, and suppose it has the equation

$$A'x' + B'y' + C' = 0,$$

where A' and B' are not both zero. The inverse image under the mapping (1) of l is then clearly the line

$$A'(a_1 x + b_1 y + c_1) + B'(a_2 x + b_2 y + c_2) + C' = 0,$$

or

$$(a_1 A' + a_2 B')x + (b_1 A' + b_2 B')y + c_1 A' + c_2 B + C' = 0,$$

or

$$Ax + By + C = 0, \tag{3}$$

where

$$A = a_1 A' + a_2 B', \qquad B = b_1 A' + b_2 B', \qquad \begin{aligned} C = c_1 A' \\ + c_2 B' + C'. \end{aligned}$$

To see that (3) is the equation of a line, it is enough to check that not both A and B are zero. But if they were, then

$$a_1 A' + a_2 B' = 0,$$

$$b_1 A' + b_2 B' = 0,$$

and it would follow from condition (2) that A' and B' were both zero. It is clear, conversely, that every point on (3) has its image under the mapping (1) on l.

We have thus proved that the mapping inverse to the given one is affine. It follows that the given mapping (1) is also affine.

Let us show now that if α is any affine transformation and it takes the point $M(x, y)$ into the point $M'(x', y')$, then the co-ordinates of M' are given in terms of those of M by linear relations of the form (1), subject to (2).

Let $O'(c_1, c_2)$, $E_1'(p_1, p_2)$, $E_2'(q_1, q_2)$ be the images of the points $O(0, 0)$, $E(1, 0)$, $E_2(0, 1)$ under the affine transformation α. In the formula (1), set

$$a_1 = p_1 - c_1, \qquad b_1 = q_1 - c_1,$$
$$a_2 = p_2 - c_2, \qquad b_2 = q_2 - c_2, \tag{4}$$

Then

$$\begin{vmatrix} a_1 & b_1 \\ a_2 & b_2 \end{vmatrix} = \begin{vmatrix} p_1 - c_1 & q_1 - c_1 \\ p_2 - c_2 & q_2 - c_2 \end{vmatrix} = \begin{vmatrix} p_1 & q_1 & c_1 \\ p_2 & q_2 & c_2 \\ 1 & 1 & 1 \end{vmatrix} \neq 0,$$

since O', E_1', E_2' are not collinear

It is easy to see that the affine transformation given by (1) (where the constants are given by (4) above) takes O, E, E_2 into O', E_1', E_2', respectively. By the theorem of Section 25, α is this affine transformation.

We have thus shown that an affine transformation is given in any coordinate system by equations of the form (1), subject to (2), and that, conversely, the transformation given by (1), subject to (2), is an affine transformation. As we did in Section 13 for orthogonal transformations, and could do (but did not) for similarity transformations (Section 19), we could prove that an affine transformation leaving the origin invariant is a linear transformation and thus show that it is represented by a system of linear equations constructively, rather than a posteriori.

It can be shown that the absolute value of Δ is the ratio in which all areas are changed by α (Section 28). For the area of $O'E_1'E_2'$ is $\frac{1}{2}|\Delta|$, so that α alters the area of OE_1E_2 by a factor $|\Delta|$. Since an affine transformation alters all areas in the same ratio (Section 28), the result follows.

Note that the coefficients in (1) depend on the particular coordinate system we choose. In a different corodinate system, Eqs. (1) would be different, but their determinant would have the same absolute value. $|\Delta|$ is thus an *invariant* of α.

As is the case for orthogonal and similarity transformations, a given affine transformation either preserves the orientation of every triangle or reverses the orientation of every triangle. We may thus speak of affine transformations of the first and second kind, and every affine transformation is either of the first or of the second kind. To prove this, we may make use of the representation theorem given in Corollary 2 to the theorem in Section 26. It is clear from this representation theorem that it is enough to show that a compression preserves the orientation of every triangle. We leave the proof of this to the reader.

It is not difficult to show that the affine transformation given by (1) above is of the first kind if Δ is positive, and of the second kind if it is negative. Thus not only $|\Delta|$ but also Δ is invariant, that is, is intrinsic to α and does not depend (as do the actual coefficients a_i, b_i, c_i in (1)) on the particular coordinate system chosen.

31. Affine Classification of Quadratic Curves

It is proved in analytic geometry that the general equation of the second degree in x and y in Cartesian coordinates represents a curve of one of the nine following forms:

ellipse:

$$\frac{x^2}{a^2} + \frac{y^2}{b^2} = 1; \tag{1}$$

imaginary ellipse:

$$\frac{x^2}{a_2} + \frac{y^2}{b^2} = -1; \tag{2}$$

two imaginary intersecting lines:

$$\frac{x^2}{a^2} + \frac{y^2}{b^2} = 0; \tag{3}$$

hyperbola:

$$\frac{x^2}{a^2} - \frac{y^2}{b^2} = 1; \qquad (4)$$

two intersecting lines:

$$\frac{x^2}{a^2} - \frac{y^2}{b^2} = 0; \qquad (5)$$

parabola:

$$y^2 = 2px; \qquad (6)$$

two parallel lines:

$$x^2 = a^2; \qquad (7)$$

two imaginary parallel lines:

$$x^2 = -a^2; \qquad (8)$$

two coincident lines:

$$x^2 = 0. \qquad (9)$$

This assertion should be understood in the following sense: that any *equation* of the second degree

$$a_{11}x^2 + 2a_{12}xy + a_{22}y^2 + 2a_{13}x + 2a_{23}y + a_{33} = 0 \quad (10)$$

can, by a suitable change of coordinates, be brought to one and only one of the nine given forms. It does not quite mean that the *curve* whose equation (in a given system of coordinates) is (10) can be made to have an equation of one and only one of the nine given forms by a suitable change of coordinates. If we wanted such a meaning for our "canonical" forms, we would have to amalgamate types (2) and (8), since they both represent the empty curve, that is, a locus containing no points whatsoever. Apart from this, however, the given classification holds also for this second interpretation.

We will now show that this classification is closely connected with the theory of affine transformations, and, in fact, coincides with the affine classification of quadratic curves (that is, curves of the second degree in each coordinate).

Definition 1. We say that two equations, each of the second degree in x and y,

$$a_{11}x^2 + 2a_{12}xy + a_{22}y^2 + 2a_{13}x + 2a_{23}y + a_{33} = 0, \quad \text{(I)}$$

$$b_{11}x^2 + 2b_{12}xy + b_{22}y^2 + 2b_{13}x + 2b_{23}y + b_{33} = 0, \quad \text{(II)}$$

belong to the same affine class, if there is a transformation

$$\begin{aligned} x' &= a_1x + b_1y + c_1, \\ y' &= a_2x + b_2y + c_2, \end{aligned} \quad \text{where} \quad \begin{vmatrix} a_1 & b_1 \\ a_2 & b_2 \end{vmatrix} \neq 0, \quad \text{(III)}$$

under which one of them is taken into the other (when we have rewritten x for x' and y for y' after the substitution).

To justify this definition, we need to show that if (I) may be obtained from (II) by such a transformation, then (II) may be obtained from (I) by another such transformation. To prove this, note that the transformation inverse to (III) (that is, the transformation giving x, y in terms of x', y') is again of the form (III).

If the condition does not hold, we say that (I) and (II) are affinely distinct.

It is more natural to talk of curves being affinely equivalent than of equations being affinely equivalent. We might phrase the definition: Two quadratic curves are affinely equivalent if and only if their Equations (I) and (II) are. There is a difficulty with this definition, however; a quadratic curve need not have a unique quadratic equation. For our purposes, the following definition will serve:

Definition 2. Two quadratic curves C_1 and C_2 are said to be affinely equivalent if neither of them is the empty set and if there are equations (I) for C_1 and (II) for C_2 that are affinely equivalent in the sense of Definition 1.

In what follows, "curve" will mean "nonempty quadratic curve" and "type" one of the types (1) to (9), but excluding (2) and (8).

Theorem I. *Two curves are affinely equivalent if and only if there is an affine transformation taking one into the other.*

Proof. Suppose the curves C_1 and C_2 are affinely equivalent. Then there are equations (I) for C_1 and (II) for C_2 that are affinely equivalent under the transformation (III). Let α be the affine transformation taking each point $M(x, y)$ of the plane into the point $M'(x', y')$ given by (III). Then clearly α takes C_1 into C_2.

Conversely, if α is an affine transformation taking C_1 into C_2, suppose that, in some coordinate system, C_1 is given by (I) and α by (III) (see Section 30). On solving (III) for x and y in terms of x' and y' and substituting in (I), we obtain an equation for C_2 (with x', y' written for x and y) that is of the form (II). By our construction, (I) and (II) are affinely equivalent. ▼

Theorem 2. *Two curves of the same type are affinely equivalent, and two curves of different types are not affinely equivalent.*

If we agree to say that two curves belong to the same affine class provided that they are affinely equivalent, then this theorem states that there is one affine class corresponding to each of the Eqs. (1) to (9). For example, two ellipses belong to the same affine class, since they are both of type (1), whereas an ellipse and any quadratic curve other than an ellipse belong to different affine classes, since they are of different types.

To prove Theorem 2, it is enough, in view of Theorem 1, to prove the following:

A. Each of two curves of the same type can be taken into the other by some affine transformation.

B. No affine transformation can take a curve of one type into a curve of another type.

Proof A. Let us show that any two ellipses are affinely equivalent. Let C_1 and C_2 be any two ellipses. Let ω be the orthogonal transformation taking the center of C_1 into the center of C_2 and the major axis of C_1 into the major axis of C_2. Suppose that, under ω, C_1 is taken into the ellipse $C_1{}^*$. Since $C_1{}^*$ and C_2 have the same center and the same axes of symmetry, their equations in the coordinate system where these axes are taken as the coordinate axes are of the form

$$\frac{x^2}{a_1{}^2} + \frac{y^2}{b_1{}^2} = 1 \qquad (C_1{}^*),$$

$$\frac{x^2}{a_2{}^2} + \frac{y^2}{b_2{}^2} = 1 \qquad (C_2).$$

The affine transformation β,

$$x = \frac{a_1}{a_2} x^*, \qquad y = \frac{b_1}{b_2} y^*,$$

takes the first of these into the second. Then $\alpha = \beta\omega$ is an affine transformation taking C_2 into C_2.

We may prove similarly that two curves of each of the other types are always affinely equivalent.

Proof B. To show that no two curves of different types are affinely equivalent, we produce a property of the curves of each type not shared by any of the other types and preserved by affine transformations: (1) is bounded, and contains more than one point; (3) contains one point; (4) is unbounded, and in two disconnected pieces; (5) is two distinct nonparallel lines; (6) is unbounded and connected; (7) is two distinct parallel lines; (9) is a single line. ▼

Theorem 3. *A quadratic equation* (I) *is affinely equivalent to one and only one of Eqs.* (1) *to* (9) *(including* (2) *and* (8)*).*

Proof. In a given coordinate system, Eq. (I) represents a conic. If it is not empty, it is affinely equivalent to just one of the types (1) to (9), and the result follows. If the conic is empty, it is affinely equivalent to one of the types (2) and (8). To show that it cannot be affinely equivalent to both, it is enough to show that Eqs. (2) and (8) themselves are not affinely equivalent. We omit the proof. ▼

We now see why we wished to exclude the empty conics from our analysis. If we allowed them in Definition 2, Theorem 2 would remain true, but there would be eight types instead of nine, all empty conics being of the same type, and we would not be able to say that two conics are affinely equivalent if and only if *any* two equations, one for each of them, are affinely equivalent. For the empty set can have either of Eqs. (2) and (8), but these equations are not affinely equivalent. The difficulty does not arise with the only other type of conic that does not have a unique equation—type (3)—because any two equations for it are affinely equivalent.

The terminology for these types, and the distinction between type (2) and (8), all become meaningful when we allow our curves to be regarded as lying in an "enriched" plane, into which we admit "points" with complex coordinates. As soon as we do this, all the "imaginary" types lose their distinction, and we have five types: ellipses and hyperbolas, parabolas, intersecting lines, parallel lines, and coincident lines. A proper discussion is beyond the scope of this book.

Just as we may give an affine classification of conics, we can give an orthogonal, or similarity, classification; that is, we can determine all the distinct classes of conics such that an orthogonal (or, as the case may be, a similarity) transformation of a conic of any one class leaves it in that class and such that, for any two conics in the same class, there is an orthogonal (or similarity) transformation taking one into the other.

For example, class (7) above is a single similarity class, since any pair of parallel lines may be taken into any other by a similarity transformation, and (6) is also a single similarity class, since any two parabolas are similar. On the other hand, class (1) splits up into an infinity of classes, one for each eccentricity. In particular, one of the classes into which (1) splits is the class of circles, all of which are similar.

When we consider orthogonal transformations, the classes split still further; for instance, the similarity class of all circles splits into an infinity of classes, one for each radius. The only orthogonal class that is a complete similarity class is (9).

In considering the similarity and orthogonal classification of conics, the difficulty we met with over empty conics arises in connection with conics of type (2) as well. For example, one equation of type (2) can be taken into another by a *similarity* change of coordinates (Eq. 3, Section 18.2) if and only if the ratio a/b is preserved. We would, therefore, like to have a separate class of "imaginary ellipses" for each such ratio; on the other hand, every such curve consists of a single point and so is equivalent, under an affine transformation, to every other such curve.

The reader may like as an exercise to give a complete orthogonal, a complete similarity, and a complete affine classification of all triangles.

Solution 1.   There is one orthogonal class for each triple of positive real numbers a, b, c such that $a + b > c$; $b + c > a$; $c + a > b$. The numbers a, b, c represent the lengths of the three sides of every triangle in a given class. The classes themselves are the various classes of congruent triangles (see Theorem 8, Section 5). We could give a different label to each class by considering a different method of proving congruence; for example, one class to each triple (a, β, γ), where a is any positive number, and $0 < \beta < \beta + \gamma < 2\pi$. Here a is the length of one side, and β and γ are the angles the other sides make with it. We identify triples that differ only in the order of the last two terms. In the first representation, we identify triples that differ only in order.

Solution 2.   There is one similarity class for each unordered pair (β, γ) where $0 < \beta < \gamma < 2\pi$ (see the theorem of Section 15).

Solution 3.   There is only one class (see the theorem of Section 25).

32. Affine Transformations of Space

Affine transformations of space are defined in precisely the corresponding manner to their definition for the plane. Just as for plane transformations, we may show that the set of all affine transformations of space form a group.

Under an affine transformation of space, the image of a line is a line, and the image of a plane is a plane. Moreover, the restriction of an affine map of space to a plane is itself an affine mapping. This may be proved in just the same way as the corresponding fact for orthogonal transformations (Section 5, Theorem 3).

Under an affine transformation of space, the images of two parallel lines are two parallel lines, and the images of two parallel planes are two parallel planes. Conversely, nonparallel lines or planes go into nonparallel lines or planes.

Under an affine transformation of space, the order of points on a line is preserved, and ratios on a given line (or on parallel lines) are preserved. This may be proved by considering the restriction of the affine mapping to any plane through the line (or the plane through the two parallel lines).

There is one and only one affine transformation of space taking four given non-coplanar points A, B, C, D into four given non-coplanar points A', B', C', D', respectively.

All these properties of affine transformations of space may be proved in the same way as the corresponding facts for affine transformations of a plane.

As examples of affine transformations of space, we may consider the subgroup of all orthogonal transformations of space or the larger subgroup of all similarity transformations of space. Other examples are compression onto a given plane with given coefficient, skew compression onto a given plane in the direction of a given line not parallel to that plane and with given coefficient, shear with given plane as axis and in the direction of a given line parallel to this plane. These transformations are defined in the obvious way by analogy with the corresponding plane transformations.

Theorem I. *An affine transformation* α *of space is the product of three compressions onto three mutually perpendicular planes and an orthogonal transformation.*

The simple proof we gave of the corresponding fact for plane transformations (Section 26) does not carry over. So we give an independent proof of this theorem.

Proof.   Consider the sphere S with center in some point O and radius R, and let O' be the image of O under the given affine transformation α of space. Let M' be the image of a given point M of S under α. Consider the set of images $O'M'$ of all the radii OM of S. Among them there will be a shortest. Let M_1 be a point of S such that the image $O'M_1'$ of OM_1 is minimal in length of all the images $O'M'$ of radii of S. Let π be the plane through M_1 perpendicular to OM_1, and let π' be its image under α. We show that π' is perpendicular to $O'M_1'$.

Suppose not, and let P' be the foot of the perpendicular from O' onto π', and P its inverse image under α. Then P lies on π (since P' lies on π'), and since P is not M_1, OP meets S in some point M lying strictly between O and P. But then the image M' of M lies strictly between O' and P', so that $O'M' < O'P' < O'M_1'$, contrary to the definition of M_1. We have thus shown that π' is perpendicular to $O'M_1'$.

Let π_1 be the plane through O parallel to π, and π_1' its image under α. Since π is parallel to π, π_1' is parallel to π' and so is perpendicular to $O'M_1'$. Suppose that π_1 meets S in the circle Σ. Denote by OM_2 a radius of Σ whose image $O'M_2'$ is of minimum length among all the images $O'M'$ of radii of Σ. We can show in the same way as before that if l is the line of π_1 through M_2 and perpendicular to OM_2, then its image l' is a line of π' perpendicular to $O'M_2'$. So the radius OM_3 of Σ perpendicular to OM_2 (and therefore parallel to l) goes into a line $O'M_3'$ lying in π_1' and perpendicular to $O'M_2'$ (since it is parallel to l'). We have thus proved the existence of three mutually perpendicular lines OM_1, OM_2, and OM_3 (through any given point of space) whose images

$O'M_1'$, $O'M_2'$, $O'M_3'$ are
also perpendicular. It follows also from this that
the three mutually perpendicular planes π_1, π_2, π_3
through O have mutual-
ly perpendicular images
π_1', π_2', π_3' through O'
(Fig. 71).

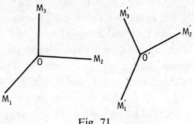

Fig. 71

Let ω be the orthogonal transformation of space that takes O
into O' and the rays OM_1, OM_2, OM_3 into the rays $O'M_1'$,
$O'M_2'$, $O'M_3'$, respectively, and let M_1^*, M_2^*, M_3^* be the
images of M_1, M_2, M_3, respectively, under ω. Let ξ_1, ξ_2, ξ_3 be
the compressions onto the planes π_1', π_2', π_3', respectively, that
take M_1^*, M_2^*, M_3^*, respectively, into M_1', M_2', M_3'. Then
the affine transformation $\xi_1\xi_2\xi_3\omega$, like α, takes the four non-
coplanar points O, M_1, M_2, M_3 into O', M_1', M_2', M_3',
respectively. By a uniqueness theorem quoted earlier in this
section, this implies that

$$\alpha = \xi_1\xi_2\xi_3\omega. \quad \blacktriangledown$$

There is one gap in our proof; we have not proved that
among the images $O'M'$ of the radii of S there will be a shortest.
To prove this, we need the following important result:

Theorem 2. *An affine transformation (of a plane or of
space) is a continuous function.*

We can give an easy proof using coordinates, because the
expression for an affine transformation in a coordinate system
is given by linear equations (see Section 30 and Eq. (1) below).
It follows that the coordinates (x', y', z') of the image point M'
of a point M under an affine transformation α are continuous
functions of the coordinates (x, y, z) of M, and a transformation
continuous in the coordinates is continuous. Or we can give a
direct proof, from the geometric properties of an affine
mapping.

We need to show that, given any neighborhood N of a point M', we can find a neighborhood P of the inverse image M of M' that maps entirely into N. Let us enclose M' by any parallelogram lying entirely inside N. Then the inverse image of the interior of this parallelogram is the interior of a parallelogram about M, so that this interior can be taken as our neighborhood P of M. The proof for affine transformations of space is similar; we take a parallelepiped instead of a parallelogram. The only properties of affine mappings we have used is that parallel lines and planes go into parallel lines and planes, and that the order of points on a line is preserved.

To show now that there is a shortest segment $O'M'$, consider the function f defined on the surface of S, whose value at each point M of S is the length of the image $O'M'$ of OM under α. Since α is, as we have proved, a continuous function, it is clear that f is continuous. Now a fundamental theorem of Weierstrass states that the image of a closed and bounded set under a continuous real-valued function is a closed and bounded subset of the real line; that is, that f has a maximum and a minimum value and that each of these values is attained at some point. Since the surface S of a sphere is a closed and bounded set, our result is now clear.

We quoted a similar result for the circle Σ, and it follows in the same way from the fact that Σ is also a closed and bounded set.

Note 1. The method we have just given for proving that any affine transformation of space can be represented as the product of an orthogonal transformation and three compressions in mutually perpendicular directions can be used to prove the corresponding result for plane affine transformations.

Note 2. Just as for affine transformations of the plane (Section 27), the coefficients of compression k_1, k_2, k_3 of ξ_1, ξ_2, ξ_3 are intrinsic to α; that is, they do not depend on the particular representation we find for α.

If the k_i are distinct, and if $k_1 < k_2 < k_3$, the directions of the compressions ξ_1, ξ_2, ξ_3 are uniquely determined: those of

ξ_1 and ξ_3 as the unique directions in which lengths are changed
by the least and the greatest ratios, and that of ξ_2 as the common perpendicular to these.

Parallel segments change their length in the same ratio, and
every length is changed in a ratio lying between k_1 and k_3.
The compressions ξ_1, ξ_2, ξ_3 are uniquely determined by α and
ω, provided that the k_i are distinct, and then are determined by
α alone up to translations. All these results may be proved in
the same way as we proved the corresponding plane results in
Section 27.

We may think of the constants k_i as the lengths of the three
principal semi-axes of the ellipsoid into which any unit sphere
is transformed by α. In the same way, we may think of the coefficients of compression k_1, k_2 of a plane affine transformation
as being the lengths of the major and minor semi-axes of the
ellipse into which any circle is taken by the transformation.

If $Oxyz$ is any affine system of coordinates in space, and the
image of any point $M(x, y, z)$ of space under the affine transformation α is the point $M'(x', y', z')$, then the coordinates of
M' are given in terms of those of M by equations of the form

$$x' = a_{11}x + a_{12}y + a_{13}z + a_1,$$

$$y' = a_{21}x + a_{22}y + a_{23}z + a_2, \qquad (1)$$

$$z' = a_{31}x + a_{32}y + a_{33}z + a_3,$$

where

$$\Delta = \begin{vmatrix} a_{11} & a_{12} & a_{13} \\ a_{21} & a_{22} & a_{23} \\ a_{31} & a_{32} & a_{33} \end{vmatrix} \neq 0. \qquad (2)$$

$|\Delta|$ is the ratio of the volume v' of the image T' of a body T
under α to the volume v of T.

Moreover, $|\Delta| = k_1 k_2 k_3$, so it is an invariant of α (that is,
its value does not change when we express α in a different
coordinate system).

We may define affine transformations of the first and second
kind in space as those that preserve the orientation of every

tetrahedron and those that reverse the orientation of every tetrahedron. Every affine transformation of space is either of the first or of the second kind. To prove this, in view of the representation theorem above and the fact that the corresponding result is true for orthogonal transformations of space (Section 11), it is enough to show that every compression onto a plane (with positive coefficient, of course) preserves the orientation of every tetrahedron. We leave the proof to the reader. The affine transformation α of space is of the first kind if and only if the determinant of its expression (1) in coordinates is positive. Thus not only $|\Delta|$ but even Δ is an invariant of α.

We may give an affine classification of quadrics (surfaces having equations of the second degree in each of the coordinates). As we did with the plane, we find it better to give a affine classification of the *equations* of the quadrics rather than the actual geometric objects. Thus the empty set is assigned to different classes according as it is regarded as having an equation of the form

$$\frac{x^2}{a^2} + \frac{y^2}{b^2} + \frac{z^2}{c^2} = -1 \qquad \text{(an imaginary ellipsoid)}$$

or an equation of the form $x^2 = -a^2$ (a pair of imaginary parallel planes). The complete list of classes is as follows: (1) ellipsoid; (2) imaginary ellipsoid; (3) imaginary cone; (4) hyperboloid of one sheet; (5) hyperboloid of two sheets; (6) cone; (7) elliptic paraboloid; (8) hyperbolic paraboloid; (9) elliptic cylinder; (10) imaginary elliptic cylinder; (11) pair of imaginary intersecting planes; (12) hyperbolic cylinder; (13) pair of intersecting planes; (14) parabolic cylinder; (15) pair of parallel planes; (16) pair of imaginary parallel planes; (17) pair of coincident planes.

Any two quadrics of the same class can be obtained from each other by an affine transformation of space. Two quadrics of different classes cannot be so obtained from each other, unless the classes are degenerate, in the sense that the quadrics in them are empty or contain a single point. A general quadratic equation in each of the three variables x, y, z can be reduced by a linear transformation (1) above to one and only one of the typical equations of the seventeen classes. We leave it to the reader to set down these typical equations and also to consider what the orthogonal and similarity classifications of quadrics should be.

We may define affine transformations in spaces of a higher number of dimensions than three, and all the obvious analogs of the theorems we have given will still hold. In particular, an affine transformation α of n-dimensional space can be represented as the product of an orthogonal transformation and n compressions onto mutually perpendicular "hyperplanes." The proof is almost word for word the same as that which we gave for the three-dimensional case. We may also consider quadratic "surfaces" in n dimensions and their affine classification, however, an attack on this problem requires a knowledge of matrix theory.

The coefficients of compression (in the three-dimensional case) can be obtained by solving the cubic equation

$$\begin{vmatrix} b_{11} - \lambda & b_{12} & b_{13} \\ b_{21} & b_{22} - \lambda & b_{23} \\ b_{31} & b_{32} & b_{33} - \lambda \end{vmatrix} = 0,$$

where the b_{ij} are the coefficients in any coordinate expression for the transformation $\alpha\omega^{-1}$ corresponding to the coefficients a_{ij} for α. Here ω is the orthogonal transformation of some representation $\alpha = \xi_1\xi_2\xi_3\omega$ of α as the product of an orthogonal transformation and three compressions in mutually perpendicular directions.

A similar result for the values of the coefficients of compression holds in any number of dimensions.

APPENDIX TO CHAPTER **II**————————

Length-Preserving Mappings

At the conclusion of Chapter II, we referred to a very elegant result due to Peter Zvengrowski (University of Chicago). Let us say a mapping α of the plane into itself *preserves distance d* provided whenever $AB = d$ we also have $A'B' = d$. Then we have the following:

Theorem. *Let α be a mapping of the plane into itself which preserves distance* 1. *Then α is an orthogonal transformation.*

Thus if α preserves one distance (other than zero), then it preserves every distance. The proof will proceed by stages.

(a) *If ABCD is a rhombus of side* 1, *then the image points A', B', C', D' are also vertices of a rhombus of side* 1.

It is clear that the triangle $A'B'C'$ is equilateral with side 1, and that D' is either the fourth vertex D_0 of the rhombus $A'B'D_0C'$, or A'. Let S be the circle with center A and radius AD, and let P be a point of S distant 1 from D. Then if $D' = A'$ we have $1 = D'P' = A'P'$. However, P is also a vertex of a rhombus of side 1 whose opposite vertex is A, so that by the same argument as for D we must have $P' = A'$ or $P' = P_0$ (in an obvious notation). But then $A'P' = 0$ or $\sqrt{3}$; in either case not 1. Thus we must have $D' = D_0$.

(b) α *preserves distance* $\sqrt{3}$.

For if $PQ = \sqrt{3}$, then P and Q are opposite vertices of some rhombus with side 1, and the result then follows from (a).

(c) *If* $\theta = 1$ *or* $\sqrt{3}$ *and n is an integer greater than* 1, *then if* $PQ \leq n\theta$ *we also have* $P'Q' \leq n\theta$.

It is clear that we may join P and Q by a zigzag line of n links, each having length θ. The images of the vertices of this configuration are vertices of a configuration of the same type, since α preserves distance θ. The result follows immediately from this.

Our next result is taken from the theory of real numbers. A proof does not, of course, fall within the scope of this book.

(d) *Let* β *be an irrational number* (say, $\sqrt{3}$). *Then given any number a, and any* $\varepsilon > 0$ (however small), *we may find arbitrarily large integers m, n such that* $a < m - n\beta < a + \varepsilon$.

(e) *We may suppose that* α *fixes the vertices* A, B, C *of an equilateral triangle of side* 1.

Let γ be the orthogonal transformation taking A, B, C to A', B', C', respectively (see Theorem 8 of Section 5). Let α′ be the mapping $\gamma^{-1}\alpha$. Since γ^{-1} and α both preserve distance 1, so also does α′. Clearly α′ fixes the points A, B, C. If we could show that α′ is the identity transformation, it would follow that $\alpha = \gamma$ is orthogonal. So we may suppose that the α with which we are working is in fact α′, and our task is now to show that α fixes *every* point.

Working outward from the triangle ABC in all directions, we can completely cover the whole plane by equilateral triangles of side 1, in such a way that any two triangles have a complete side in common, one vertex in common, or nothing in common. Such a decomposition of the plane is called a *triangulation*. Let us call the vertices of the triangles the *lattice points*, and the lines of the triangulation the *lattice lines*.

(f)   α *fixes every lattice point.*

Certainly α fixes A, B, C. As we work out from the triangle ABC, each new lattice point we reach is the fourth vertex of a rhombus of side 1 whose other vertices we have already dealt with. So at each step we can conclude from (a) that our vertex is fixed.

We now aim to show that α fixes every point of every lattice line. Let X be any point on any lattice line p.

Let $\alpha(X) = X'$, and suppose that the perpendicular from X' to p meets p in X_0.

(g) $X_0 = X$.

Suppose $X_0 \neq X$; choose a lattice point O on p such that X_0 lies between O and X. Introduce coordinates on p by taking O as origin and assigning X the *positive* coordinate x $(x = OX)$. We shall think of p as horizontal, with X lying to the right of O. We write $X = X(x)$, and we shall use a similar notation for the other points on p that we shall be introducing.

If $X_0 = X_0(x_0)$, then $x_0 < x$ by our choice of coordinate system. By (d) we may choose integers m, n such that $m > x$, $n > 1$, and $x_0 < m - n\sqrt{3} < x$. Now let $M = M(m)$, $N = N(m - n\sqrt{3})$. Then O, X_0, N, X, M occur in that order along

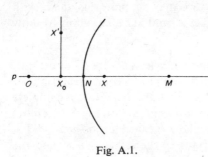

Fig. A.1.

p. Next, $MX < MN = n\sqrt{3}$, with $n > 1$. Also M is a lattice point, and so is fixed. Thus by (c) $MX' = M'X' \leq n\sqrt{3}$, so that X' lies inside or on the circle with center M and radius MN. As we see from Fig. A.1, this is impossible.

(h) $X' = X$.

We see from (g) that X' lies on the perpendicular q through X to p. If $X' \neq X$, we can find a positive number ε so small that $\varepsilon < 2$, $4\varepsilon < XX'$. Now by (d) choose integers m_0, n_0 such that $n_0 > 1$ and $x - 2 < m_0 - n_0\sqrt{3} < x - 2 + \varepsilon < x$. Set $Y = Y(x - 2)$, $N_0 = N_0(m_0 - n_0\sqrt{3})$, $Z = Z(x - 2 + \varepsilon)$, $M_0 = M_0(m_0)$. Then the points Y, N_0, Z, X occur in that order along p.

M_0 is a lattice point, and so fixed, and $M_0 N_0 = n_0\sqrt{3}$. We conclude by (c) that the image N' of N_0 lies inside or on the circle L with center M_0 and radius $n_0\sqrt{3} = M_0 N_0$. But we also know from (g) that N' lies on the perpendicular t through N_0 to p. It follows that $N' = N_0$, so that N_0 is a fixed point.

Now let S be the circle with center N_0 and radius 2 (see Fig. A.2). If S meets q in U and V, we easily see that

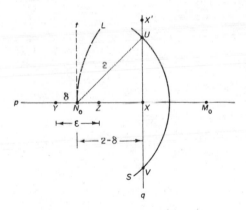

Fig. A.2.

$XU = XV = 4\delta - \delta^2 < 4\delta < 4\varepsilon < XX'$, where $\delta = YN_0 < YZ = \varepsilon$. Thus X' lies *outside* S. On the other hand $N_0 X = 2 - \delta < 2.1$, so that by (c) $N_0 X' \leq 2$, and X' lies *inside* (or on) S. This contradiction shows that $X' \neq X$ is impossible.

(i)   α *fixes every point.*

Let P be any point of the plane, and let T be the circle with center P and radius 1. Clearly T will meet lattice lines in at least three distinct points, say J, K, L. Then T' will be at distance 1 from J', K', L'. Since by (h) $J' = J$, $K' = K$, $L' = L$, we must have $P' = P$.

As we explained after (e), this completes the proof of the theorem.

Subject Index

tr. = transformation(s).

References with page numbers in parentheses are to relevant passages in which, however, the actual *words* in the index do not appear.